MW00564645

ABENAKI WARRIOR

The Life and Times of CHIEF ESCUMBUIT

Big Island Pond 1665-1727

French Hero! British Monster! Indian Patriot!

Alfred E. Kayworth

Library of Congress Cataloging-in-Publication Data

Kayworth, Alfred E.
Abenaki warrior : the life and times of Chief Escumbuit, Big Island Pond, 1665-1727 : French hero! British monster! Indian patriot! / Alfred E. Kayworth.
p. cm.
Includes bibliographical references and index.
ISBN 0-8283-2032-2 (alk. paper)
1. Escumbuit, Abenaki chief, 1665-1727.
2. Abenaki Indians--Kings and rulers--Biography.
3. Abenaki Indians--Wars.
4. Abenaki Indians--Government relations.
I. Title.
E99.A13.E735 1998
973.2'6--dc21 97-48674
[B] CIP

BRANDEN PUBLISHING COMPANY
17 Station Street
Box 843 Brookline Village
Boston, MA 02147

To the ABENAKI INDIANS

Of Maine, New Hampshire, Vermont, and Canada

Your ancestor, Chief Assacumbuit, is the principal character of this work. Many of the events were taken from history books that tell of the long wars between the Abenaki Indians and the Europeans.

The historical footnotes are important to the narrative, since they describe and confirm the Sachem's leading role in the border wars with the English from 1688 to 1708.

He was a War Chief and Sachem of the Pigwacket Tribe when his name first began to appear in English and French accounts. His boyhood exploits with his tribe at the headwaters of the Saco River are simply a representation of what he might have been like as a young brave. The essential facts are confirmed by English and French historians. Some of his actions, however, as well as his thoughts and motives, are my creation, added to provide a sense of human interest. But the exploits that brought him fame are all true!

Your ancestors roamed the mountains, valleys, rivers and seacoasts of New England long before the arrival of the Europeans. It has been 271 years since the Spirit of Chief Assacumbuit began his journey to a special place created for the Indians by the Great Spirit. Yet, the history of the Abenaki people reaches far back into the dim mists of time--perhaps as far back as 12,000 years.

Thousands of lesser men have had their life story recorded for posterity. It is appropriate that the famous Indian warrior and patriot--Assacumbuit--now assume his rightful place in history.

May his Spirit take comfort from this overdue recognition of his fame.

The former Attorney General of the State of Massachusetts, Francis X. Bellotti, rendered this opinion:

"I believe this book will stand as a magnificent memorial to Chief Escumbuit and to the Abenaki Indians."

It is also my wish that it be so.

ALFRED E. KAYWORTH

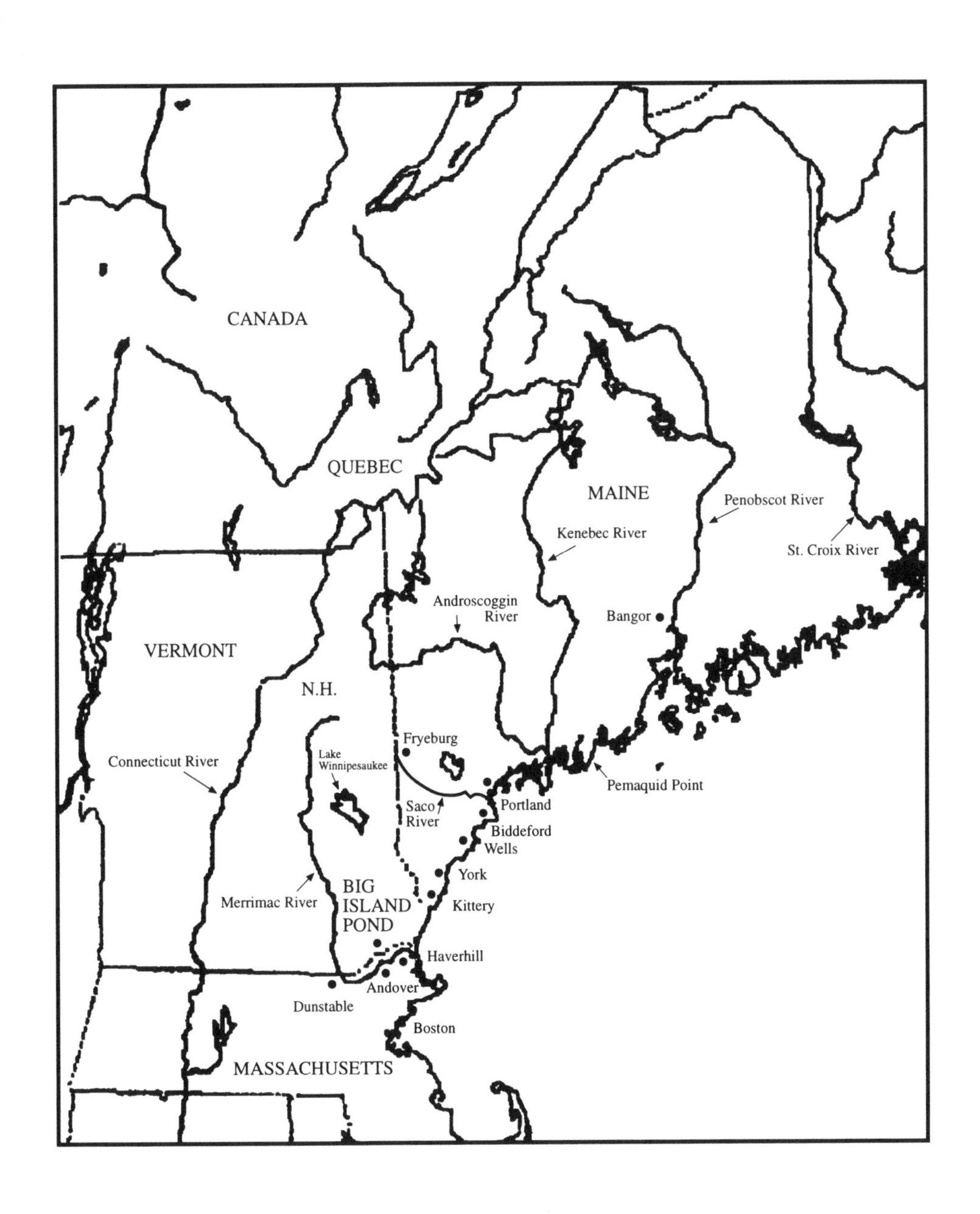
CANADA
QUEBEC
MAINE
Penobscot River
Kenebec River
St. Croix River
Androscoggin River
Bangor
VERMONT
N.H.
Fryeburg
Lake Winnipesaukee
Connecticut River
Pemaquid Point
Portland
Saco River
Biddeford
Wells
York
BIG ISLAND POND
Merrimac River
Kittery
Haverhill
Andover
Dunstable
Boston
MASSACHUSETTS

CONTENTS

Escumbuit--His life story reads like fiction!

- Fought the English from Andover, Massachusetts to Newfoundland
- His famous war club boasted 98 notches
- Knighted by King Louis XIV of France at the Palace of Versailles
- Presented with silver saber and given pension for life by the King of France
- Favorite of French élite during one year visit to France
- Credited with the death of 150 English Settlers
- Discovered silver mine in White Mountains of New Hampshire
- Banished for murder by his Pigwacket Tribe
- Found sanctuary at Big Island Pond in Derry, New Hampshire
- Wounded in the 1708 raid on Haverhill, Massachusetts
- Abandoned by the French, he sought wealth through his silver mine

Author's note: Although this story is based on actual historical events covered by English and French historians in which they describe the role taken by the Indian Chief variously known as Escumbuit, Assacumbuit and Nescambiouit, many of the details, including the description of his boyhood, are a product of the author's imagination. The main events in his life, such as his raids on the coastal settlements and Newfoundland and attacks on Andover and Haverhill, are true and are confirmed in footnotes. His visit to France and the date and circumstances of his death are also taken from historical references.

For my daughter
Tami Jo

After a spectacular day on Escumbuit Island, I took my phone to the pine-covered knoll facing the lake and the setting sun. I called Tami in Loxahatchee, Florida and said:

"Tami, it is so beautiful here that I wanted to share it; and, knowing how you love the island, I thought of you."

Then, from my sitting position on the pine needles, I described my surroundings and evolving scene as the sun sank below the ridge lines across the lake. When I finished, she said:

"Dad, I feel like I'm there with you. You really ought to sit down at your computer and put that description on paper. I know you can do it!"

That scene appears later on these pages.

And to the girl who urged me to write, I dedicate this book.

Alfred Kayworth

FOREWORD

Escumbuit Island first attracted my attention when my mother allowed me to camp out at Chases' Grove, Big Island Pond, NH in 1934. Prior to that I was a guest of the Korb and Minzner families beginning in about 1928. The Chase family had a small variety store on the lake front and a dance hall in its present location. They allowed people to pitch tents and camp in the woods up behind the store and we called this area "Hobo Lodge." This was the beginning of my life long love affair with my favorite place.

My preparations began with a raid on my mother's pantry in our second story tenement on Milk Street, Methuen, Massachusetts. There, after packing a small hand bag with a few assorted canned goods, my bathing suit and tooth brush, I'd announce to my mother:

"Mom, I'm hitch hiking up to the lake and I'll be staying at Hobo Lodge."

"When will you be home?" she would ask.

And I'd say, "I've got fifty cents. When that's gone I'll be back."

With that, I was on my way with mother's admonition: "Be careful."

Besides my little stash of canned goods, I had a box of Quaker Oats. A pint of unpasteurized milk cost me five cents down at Chase's store. If I had nothing else, I could boil up a mess of oats and eat it with my five cent a bottle milk. No--I didn't really exist on canned goods, Quaker

Oats and milk. Invariably, some of the good folks tenting out at Hobo Lodge would take pity on the 14-year-old kid, who seemed to own nothing but the swimming trunks he wore. Usually, someone would offer me a sandwich at noon, a warm meal in the evening and a blanket and a corner of their tent at night. Mom never did figure out how I could spend a week at the lake on 50 cents.

I *loved* Hobo Lodge. It became my summer hang-out. Labor day we had swimming races and I used to look forward to the canoe tilting contest. I stood on the thwarts up forward with a long bamboo pole with a padded tip. With my partner paddling in the back seat, the object was to push my opponent on the opposing canoe into the water. When I was 16 years old, I remember being knocked off my perch in the finals by a boy named Alan Shepard.

I saw this kid swimming with a rope harness around his shoulders pulling an empty row boat just off the little island opposite Chase's Grove. He lived in the white camp facing the broad reach of the lake. At the time, I thought to myself, "What in the world is that kid training for?"

It would be many years before my question would be answered as I sat, transfixed, in front of my television watching this same *kid* hit a golf ball off the surface of the moon. Now an Admiral, Alan B. Shepard is renown as the first American in space.

In those days, we called it *Shepard's Island;* but I later learned that it was also known as *Escumbuit Island.* This was my first encounter with the name which has fascinated me for all these years.

Some 60 years later, I spend my summers at the camp next door to the Shepard cottage on Escumbuit Island. I bought the property from my friend, Arthur McEvoy, in the mid eighties. Then with the expert help of my friend, Bill Banton and some 'sweat equity,' I created my own Hobo Lodge. There, with the modern comforts of electricity, telephone, satellite television and a computer, I was 16 again--almost!

When I arrived on Escumbuit Island from my home in Boca Raton, Florida in May of 1996, I came with a plan to write a story about Big Island Pond. When I mentioned my interest in the subject to Herb Lippold, President of the Big Island Pond Association, he suggested that I talk to Wally Williams, editor of *The Island Pond Ponderables*. Wally referred me to 'Patsy' Goodridge, a director of the Association. She lives on the lake in Hemlock Heights with her husband, Al, writes poetry and has done a lot of research on Big Island Pond.

When I contacted her, it was apparent she had accumulated a great deal of information about the lake, on Chief Escumbuit and on the Indians of New England in general. Although she had a project of her own in mind, she was quite generous in pointing me in the right direction, recommending a few libraries and giving me a few keys to get me started. As I put in 100 or more hours visiting and researching libraries and historical societies from Concord, New Hampshire, to Andover, Massachusetts, I always checked back with Patsy. It was fun to test my ideas on someone with so much knowledge. Her interest and encouragement were a big help.

My research on Chief Escumbuit uncovered so much interesting material that I finally decided a story about his extraordinary life could stand on its own. The remaining decision was: in what form should I tell the story? After reading many books written by French and English historians, I decided it would make a more interesting narrative to relate the historical details against the background of the Abenaki culture I had studied with interest during the summer. It meant that I would have to fill in the gaps in his life for which there is no recorded history. Once I began to improvise, it could no longer be called a history of the life of Chief Escumbuit.

My search for information on Escumbuit led me to a larger story of the war that raged for almost a 100 years between the French, the Indians and the British Colonists. None of these combatants were completely guiltless. I have tried to be objective in my presentation of the facts, but the nature of some of the material makes that difficult.

I want to thank Wally and Mary Lou Williams for the excellent editing job they did on my completed story. Their red pencil corrections and suggestions were invariably on target. Their long time association with the lake and their intimate knowledge of its history are well known. This made *their* approval and encouragement of my efforts all the more rewarding.

Glenda Schaake, head of reference at the Andover Library, literally provided the key to the elusive details of the 1698 Indian attack on Andover, Massachusetts. The key words were Pasco Chubb and were locked away in her small historical reading room. Finally, I had the true facts behind Pasco Chubb's demise! Thank you, Glenda.

The translated works of the Reverend P. F. X. de Charlevoix, S. J. eluded me until Marilyn Dent suggested I try St. Anselms College in Manchester, New Hampshire. For that and other assistance, I thank Marilyn and the Derry Public Library.

Dennis Brown and Barry Masterson are knowledgeable Maine State Bureau of Parks and Recreation rangers at the Historical Restoration Site at Pemaquid. They helped me correct inaccuracies in my accounts of the 1689 and 1696 French and Indian attacks on the fort. My best wishes to them and I hope to visit with them again.

Peter Kayworth's objective critique of the original manuscript was on target. There was a need to cue the reader when using flashbacks in my story; separating the historical quotes from the text simplified my narrative style. Thanks Pete!

Patty Taylor, secretary to the Chief of Police of Delray Beach, Florida, detected a series of typos that needed editing. Detective Robert *Cagney* Stevens and his girl friend, Tami Jo Kayworth, said she was good; and she is! Thank you, Patty.

My story came to the attention of Branden Publishing Company in a strange way. My island neighbor, to whom I gave a copy of the rough manuscript, in turn loaned the copy to a resident whose cottage on the mainland faces us across the channel. I punched the button on the answering machine, and there: "My name is Maggie Starrett. I read a copy of your story given to me by Karen Wilkins, and I am fascinated by it. I have a friend who is a publisher, and he would like to talk with you about it."

I played the message three times, thinking this has got to be a hoax! But I returned her call, and within an hour, I was sitting on her boat dock, sipping wine and talking in Spanish with Adolph *Adolfo* Caso, the publisher and the author of fifteen books. What a heady experience!

That meeting began an adventure that I never could have imagined much less anticipated. Maggie, how can I ever thank you enough? And to you, Adolfo, whose writing skills I can only aspire to approximate: *mil gracias y buena suerte.*

For a brief period in his life, Chief Escumbuit was both famous and infamous depending on whether you want to believe the French or the English historians. My research revealed that he was widely known, not only to English historians, but his fame had spread to France as well. Why was the lake called *Lake Escumbuit* as late as 1926? This historical novel, if it can be called that, attempts to answer that question. To me, Chief Escumbuit--vilified by the English Colonists--idolized by the French--deserves a place in history. It is for you, the reader, to decide how Escumbuit should be remembered.

INTRODUCTION

This is a story about Chief Escumbuit, Abenaki Indian, for whom a small island at Big Island Pond, Derry, New Hampshire, is named. The Abenaki Indians claimed the areas of Maine, New Hampshire and Vermont as their ancestral home since pre-historic time. The Abenaki Indians shared a common language called Algonquian, but the spoken dialects differed according to the location of the individual tribes whose names generally described the area where their village was located.

Escumbuit, a Pigwacket Indian, came from the headwaters of the Saco River in Maine from the general area of Fryeburg. This area, just east of Conway, sits in a beautiful valley attended by the White Mountains in the west. Replete with forests, lakes, and natural interval land for farming, its final bonus was its accessibility to the Atlantic Ocean via the Saco River.

The story describes in some detail how Escumbuit was raised from childhood to conform to the Indian code of conduct, which was simple and rigorous at the same time. The Spartan virtues--to speak the truth, to scorn fear and exalt valor, to endure and to repay in kind good for good and evil for evil--were the mark of a man and a warrior.

The span of Escumbuit's life (1665 to 1727) was marked by almost continuous warfare between the French, their Abenaki Indian allies, the English Colonists and their Iroquois Indian allies.

From the beginning, Escumbuit stands out from his fellow braves as the most courageous, the most daring and the most bloodthirsty of them all. Early on, as he strove to prove his mettle to the French and his fellow braves, his ability was recognized and marked for important things. In the modern vernacular, he was a comer. At a young age, he was chosen by his fellow braves to be a *War Chief* of his Pigwacket Tribe.

By 1690, he was involved in many of the French sponsored raids against English border settlements. In 1696, both English and French accounts began to single him out in individual actions described in some detail in this story. He continued to cut new notches on his famous war club and his reputation continued to grow.

After his achievements with the French commanders, D'Iberville and Montigny at St. Johns, Newfoundland, his exploits came to the attention of King Louis XIV, who micro-managed the war from his palace at Versailles, France. In summoning Captain Sieur de Montigny to France to receive honors, the King ordered that Chief Escumbuit also appear before him.

Escumbuit, with Montigny as his mentor, was received by the King at his lavish court at the Palace of Versailles, where he delighted King Louis XIV with an account of his exploits against the King's enemies, resulting in his being knighted and given a silver handled sabre together with a lifelong pension and other gifts. During his extended stay in Paris, he was feted by the French people and honored by the élite. He became familiar with such famous French products as wine, clothes, horse-drawn carriages, as well as other things such as tall buildings which utterly impressed him. Then there were the elegant

French women, who admired him for his physical prowess, his demeanor, and comportment. He also met Charlesvoi, the famous French historian bent on telling as complete a story as possible about the various activities taking place in the New World.

In 1707, after spending a year with the French, Escumbuit returned to his village in Maine--a changed man. Penhallow, the English historian, noted that on his return, Escumbuit attempted to exert his sovereignty over his fellow tribesmen. Involved in a fight, he stabbed one of the braves to death and severely wounded another. Heeding the vengeance that was sure to follow by the relatives of the victims, he was forced to leave his tribe forever.

He began a new life with a small isolated band of displaced Indians at the place now called Big Island Pond, presently touching the borders of Atkinson, Derry, and Hampstead, New Hampshire. Having operated from this base in raids against the border settlements, he felt secure here from both the English and his Pigwacket enemies.

The following year, he performed great deeds of valor with the French in their raid on the village of Haverhill, Massachusetts, where he was wounded in the foot by a musket ball. Attended by his new wife and a shaman, he recovered. However, this superb physical specimen was no longer able to run; indeed, he walked with a distinct limp.

In his declining years, he was frustrated in not being in the lime light, and died while attempting to achieve fame through a failed commercial venture with an English trader.

In his youth, he stumbled upon a silver mine but refused to reveal its location to anyone, hoping that in time, he would lay claim to it and become a wealthy man. Throughout his life, he stubbornly guarded his secret--a secret that would also reveal one of the intriguing mysteries of the war between the Indians and the Colonists.

ESCUMBUIT ISLAND 1725

Chief Escumbuit sat on his low pallet, his back resting against the butt of a large pine tree, watching the play of the naked boys down the slope toward the lake. The group of 12 boys ranged in age from four to ten. It was common for Indian children of both sexes to go naked about the camp until about the age of ten. After that, they assumed the modesty of the adults and dressed accordingly.

The older boys had bows and arrows and they were shooting at a mat up the slope about 25 strides away. Small silhouettes of deer, bear, rabbits and squirrels were crudely drawn on a rough mat made of woven cat-tails gathered from the swampy area down the lake. Mats like these were used in the winter to insulate the inside of the wigwams and the long house where the Indians took shelter from the cold.

"How excited and proud I was when I was given my first bow and arrows", Chief Escumbuit thought. "I was five years old and my uncle showed me how to care for them. He showed me how to brace the tip of the bow against the inside of my foot; then bend it in order to put the cord in the notch of the bow. He taught me how to hold, aim, and shoot my arrows. I must never aim and draw my bow unless I mean to kill. Even in practice I was to think of killing with each shot. Yes, all my friends had been given their first bow and arrows at the same age. Only with a bow and arrows could one be a true brave."

The boys chattered and yelped in delight on hitting the figures with their arrows; and, with an especially good shot, they would look toward the Chief to see if he was watching. Studying his moccasin clad left foot, he continued: "The most powerful spells and magic of the greatest Shamen have failed to make my foot whole as the feet of the children before me are whole. I would give up much of my fame as a warrior to be able to leap and run like them. Indeed, I would endure the torture of the Iroquois to walk once again without the limp of a wounded deer."

The year was 1725 in the Indian lunar month of *Nokkaekas* (June, when the corn was hoed). The month past was *Kikas* (May, when corn was planted) and the coming month would be *Sataikas* (July, when the blueberries were ripe). This was how Indians understood words--as pictures referring to familiar activities.

The women went to the tribal garden located in the bowl shaped area which led to the outlet for the waters of the lake. The soil was rich and fertile, and the garden, several acres in size, produced vegetables such as squash, pumpkins, beans, sunflowers and tobacco. Their cornfield was on the higher ground, 200 yards to the north. The Indians learned over time that corn needed different soil.

The women brought the younger children and babies with them, the very young strapped to cradle boards, their bodies held in a straight position, so restrained until they were able to sit erect on their own, and were hung in hammocks woven of cordage made from the inner bark of elm and basswood trees.

The hammocks were lined with swamp rushes and dried corn husks which were saved and used for many different things. They went into padding for sleeping pallets in the wigwam and the long house. The dried corn silk worked well as finger and mouth wipes when eating. The older children were required to stay close to their mother as she hoed and pulled weeds in the community garden. Some of the women used metal hoes they had gotten through trade with the white man, but many still used the deer's shoulder blade bound to a wooden handle with raw-hide thongs. Still others used hoes made from turtle shells.

Two young braves were sent to watch for raiding parties coming from the south. At the south end of the lake the land rose to a ridge and the 15-year-old braves patrolled this ridge and the land to the south and west to make sure that the women would have time to run back to the island in case of an attack.

The preparation of this garden was relatively easy. The Indians traded with the white man for steel axes to cut the few trees standing in this low lying area. Before the white man came, trees were felled by burning.

Before acquiring the white man's steel tools, the Indians lit fires close to the base of a series of trees, concentrating the flames by building small walls of clay or mud around the tree. As the fire died down, they cut out the charred wood with their dull stone axes until fresh wood was exposed. Alternating between fire making and chopping enabled them to fell trees and create the clearings they needed to establish their gardens.[1]

The Chief's wife, his daughter and granddaughter worked together hoeing and weeding squash and pumpkin plants that were already putting out strong runners. When

---

[1] The Indian How Book, Arthur C. Parker, (p. 56)

fully grown, these would become part of the regular daily fare. What they could not eat right away would be cut into thin strips, dried in the sun and stored in bark containers placed in holes in the ground to be eaten during the lean winter months.

They each wore deerskin skirts made of rectangular pieces of deer skin, wrapped and supported by thongs tied around the waist with a slit on one side to permit freedom of movement. Over that they wore shirts of deerskin, and wore moose skin moccasins on their feet.

The long hair of the older woman was collected in a single braid which hung down her back. The 12-year-old girl had her hair arranged in two braids. Metaxta, the grandmother, stood about 5' 2" in height; although she was in her late 40's, her hair was still black and shone with the bear grease she had applied to it that morning. Although her body was thick, she was not fat and the wrinkles around her eyes and mouth were the only signs of aging. Her daughter, except for being slightly taller, favored her mother in most ways. Though slender, the girl was as tall as her grandmother with the promise of being the tallest of the three in time.

Metaxta rested on her hoe for a moment and said to her granddaughter, "Bluebird--the sun is at the top of the trees on the ridge. It is time to return to the island. Go see if the good spirit has sent a bird to the snare which we set this morning. Your mother and I will finish hoeing this row and we will meet you at the canoe. Don't forget to bring the ground tubers and the fern shoots that are in the basket near the snare."

The young girl, happy with the break from the hard work, dropped her hoe and set off running, calling over her shoulder, "Yes, grandmother, I will meet you and mother at the canoe."

The grandmother, turning to her daughter commented, "She runs and thinks like a child, but she will soon show the sign that she is becoming a woman. We must prepare a separate wigwam for her ceremony of womanhood to keep her apart from the boys."

They returned to their hoeing at a brisk pace in anticipation of returning to the island and the refreshing bath that awaited them in the lake.

The division of work among the Indians was set by age old customs. The men trapped and hunted the meat bearing animals; they also fished, netted and speared the fish. They built the wigwams, the long houses and the canoes and fashioned the farming utensils and the flint arrow and spear heads for their hunting equipment. It was also their job to go on the war path.

The women tended the garden, cured the hides of the deer and moose, helped tap the maple trees in the spring, dried the vegetables, meat and fish over their cooking fires and prepared the food. Although the men built the wigwams, these were the property of the women who occupied the wigwam. The Indian male was there by her forbearance, and if she wanted him to leave, he must take only his personal belongings. The wigwam was the property of the squaw.

To the casual visitor to an Abenaki village, it might appear that the women were mistreated by the men as they always appeared to be working. In fact, the Abenaki treated the women with great respect and took great pride in their wives' ability to keep orderly wigwams, to cook, weave baskets and make clothing.

Abenaki Indian families were extremely close knit. Each family inherited a family totem which was handed down from generation to generation. This totem was generally some type of animal, a bird, or a fish and the members of a family were thought to have some of the desirable traits of their totem. For example, families with the squirrel totem were thought to be quick and intelligent. The owl totem represented great wisdom.

Indians believed in the immortality of all living things. When an Indian stalked and killed a deer, he would take a moment to talk to the spirit of the dead animal to explain how sorry he was, that it had been necessary to kill him. He might wish the spirit of the dead animal good fortune in his new life which would be created for him by Gluskap, the great spirit who created and controlled all living things. He would explain that it was necessary to kill him in order to feed his people and to use his sinews to sew and his hide to clothe the Indians.

The lives of all Indians were controlled to a great extent by good and bad spirits. Important events such as marriages, deaths, and decisions to go on the war path, were marked by ceremonies which included singing and chanting accompanied by drums and other noisemakers.

Two women worked on the hide of a large buck deer taken on the big island the previous week.

A young brave had spotted the deer browsing on the shore while fishing with drop lines from their canoe. The braves organized quickly. They sent a killing party to the far end of the island where the large flat rock sloped to the water. Braves in two canoes were sent to patrol the south shore of the island to prevent the deer from crossing the short span of water to the mainland. The remainder formed a driving line with drums and other noise makers which slowly drove the deer to the north end of the island where he was killed with a single shot by one of the waiting braves. The deer had twice attempted to cross to the mainland, but was driven back by the yells and drums of the braves patrolling the south shore of the island in their canoes.

This driving method was a common way of taking deer and elk long before they had the white man's *thunder stick*. They erected long V-shaped palisades in the woods with a small opening at the point of the V. About 12 feet in back of the opening, another short V was built. As the deer were driven into the point by a line of braves, some would attempt to exit the opening. When they encountered the second palisade, they had to turn left or right where the waiting braves brought them down with their spears.

Now, as the Chief watched, the two women were working the hide in the traditional Indian way. It was soaked in water for several days, the hair side sprinkled with lye made from wood ashes. Now, they placed the skin over a *graining log* which was a large debarked log buried obliquely in the ground so that the top was about waist high. Placing the hair side down, they had removed all of the bits of flesh, sinew and fat with a metal scraper. On turning the hair side up, they began the process of scraping off the lye and loosened the hair with a beaming tool, being very careful not to work a thin spot in the skin.

"My uncle told me how my ancestors prepared deer hides", thought the Chief as he turned to watch more closely. "They did not have the white man's tools. They used a sharp piece of flint to scrape off the fat and they scraped the hair with a sharp bone of the deer. The women must now wash and stretch it to make a fine, soft buckskin."

The skin was now washed and wrung out several times in preparation for *framing*. Then the washed skin was stretched very tightly inside an open wooden frame with cords fashioned from inner bark fibers of the elm. Once the skin dried, a solution made by mixing deer brains, liver paste and warm water was rubbed into the hide until completely saturated. After the skin was removed from the frame, it was put through a lengthy working process. It was soaked, removed, tied to a tree and twisted with a stick until all the moisture was wrung out, the process repeated several times until the cellular fiber was removed leaving a clean sheet of pelt fiber.

When this soft, pliable, white skin was ready for the final coloring process, it was sewed into an irregular cone shape with all openings sewn shut. Held open by sticks, it was suspended over a smudge fire to fill the skin with smoke. It required much care to keep the smudge going constantly and evenly until the right color--yellow, tan or brown was achieved. The skin was then laid away for a few days until the color set.[2]

The Chief's attention was suddenly drawn to the sound of muted voices coming from the mainland. He sat in the sun wearing only his breech cloth and moccasins. As he pulled himself erect, he appeared quite tall for an Indian--

---

[2] The Indian How Book, Arthur C. Parker, (p.70-76) Describes the Indian method of "working" a green hide into buckskin as opposed to the "tanning" process.

a full six feet in height. In spite of being old, in Indian terms, his physique was still impressive. He had the broad shoulders of a long-distance swimmer, and his legs were very muscular, a result of many years walking long distances carrying heavy loads on his back.

Closer inspection revealed numerous scars marring the dark reddish brown color of his skin. These scars, better than anything, offered evidence of his life-long struggle as an Abenaki warrior fighting the Iroquois and the English.

As he looked intently across the lake, the late sun lit his face. His cheek bones were prominent--the dark brown eyes piercing--the hairless face gaunt, with crow feet wrinkles at the eyes and the sides of his mouth. His head was shaved except for the prominent top-notch on the back of his head in which were inserted the two feathers identifying him as an Abenaki warrior. His most striking feature, besides his eyes, were his hawk-like nose which was prominent and slightly arched like that of an eagle. He suddenly spoke.

"The women return from the garden now. It is time for me to bathe."

He walked down the slope, but the lack of flexibility in his rigid ankle forced him into a pronounced limp. The two squaws stepped back from their work on the deer hide and silently watched his awkward progress over the rocks to the water's edge.

Shaking her head, one remarked to her companion, "Our Chief is as the captured eagle, bound to his perch by rawhide thongs. His heart is still fierce, but his wings cannot carry him to his former heights."

Her companion responded, "Yes, my heart lies heavy in my breast to see our chief so."

Almost as if he heard the squaw's short discussion, Chief Escumbuit soaped his torso and thought: "What spirits have I offended that I must live as an elder--eating, but not hunting--living, but unable to make war on the enemies of my people. I fought the English many moons and I have many scars on my body from Iroquois spears and tomahawks. My thigh shows where I was struck by an English musket ball and my shoulder shows the mark of the sabre cut I took from the English. My warriors chanted in the powwow before many battles that death could not claim me. Then came the English musket ball to my foot at Haverhill which put a lie to all the boasts of my fellow warriors. Better that death come to my wigwam, take my hand, and lead me to the other world than exist as I am now. I am no longer a warrior. I am not even a squaw for I cannot work."

Presently, his wife Metaxta came to join him in the shallow water where he sat with the water up to his armpits. She untied her thong which held up the deerskin skirt she was wearing while working in the garden. Then she removed the skirt and placed a stone on it to hold it under water to soak while she soaped her own body to remove the dirt she accumulated during the day. She then undid the single braid which hung down her back, and, sitting in the water to her shoulders, she inclined her head to wash the long black hair which hung below the level of her shoulders. After it dried, she applied bear fat to it and her daughter Ramona would braid it for her.

Metaxta was the Chief's second wife. She had accepted his proposal to marriage soon after he joined their small band 19 years earlier. After his banishment from the Pigwacket Tribe, he came to this place. From here he raided the settlements of the English until he was wounded at Haverhill. She recognized the Chief's love for his former home, but gradually saw that love flow to her family, to her tribe and to that lake. Now he had become a Pawtucket like her, but never completely. He still carried the savagery of the Pigwacket in his blood.

Indians were far from being the *unwashed savages* described by early historians. All of the Woodland Indians lived near lakes or streams where water was plentiful and they took full advantage of it. New-born babies were given cold water baths shortly after birth and Indian boys in the northeast were given baths almost every day of the year, even in winter. The elders chopped holes in the ice and the boys were required to jump into the almost freezing water. To be sure, they were out in a flash, exclaiming, "Ah-tcoo, o-to-weh!" which might translate into, "Wow, that's cold!"

They were also required to take *snow rubs* and *sweat baths*. The sweat bath, taken about twice a year, was used primarily to drive out demons.

The sweat lodge was about six feet in diameter and about four feet tall, formed by flexible boughs covered with braided swamp rushes, bark and sometimes animal skins to hold in the steam. In front of the tent opening, stones were heated over a fire until they were white hot. The naked brave sat inside with a container full of water and a dipper. He reached outside with a hooked stick and pulled the hot stones into the central pit after which he closed the door and poured water over them. The resulting steam and heat in the enclosed space were so intense that it took much will power to stay inside the hut. Outside, the medicine man chanted his supplications to the spirits to drive poisons, diseases and other demons from their bodies. When the brave inside could no longer stand the heat, the steam and the lack of oxygen, he would run outside and plunge into the open water. This treatment was so debilitating that the brave would usually go to his wigwam to sleep for a while after which he would emerge feeling cleansed.

Warriors preparing for a hunt would routinely take medicines which would cause them to void their bowels. They took warm baths in large bark tubs into which certain sweet smelling leaves and ferns were added, believing this procedure necessary to remove all trace of human odor which might betray them to the game they expected to be stalking. They went to great pains to remove all traces of human smell when they prepared the various types of snares, dead falls and traps they used. Everything they made with their hands, to be used in the woods to trap animals, was washed or smoked to remove traces of human smell.

After bathing, the Chief and Metaxta went up to their wigwam located in the center of the knoll to offer a sweeping view of the lake to the west, north and east. After putting on a clean breech cloth and shirt, the Chief sat cross-legged on a low pallet near the cooking fire. Metaxta described the progress of the vegetable garden and told him that she snared a partridge close to where they were working.

Similar scenes took place on various parts of the island where individual families set up their summer wigwams for a welcome change from living in the long house. The long house was built in the saddle between two knolls on the north end of the island. Beyond the second knoll, the ground sloped down to lake level at the eastern-most end of the island. This saddle had a flat area about 100 feet square on which the Indians built a long house about 12 feet wide by 60 feet long. It had entrance doors at either end and a series of smoke holes in the domed roof to vent the cooking fires used during the winter. During the cold weather, the north opening would be closed off and insulated against the cold north winds sweeping down the lake. However, the opening on the south end was kept open. All of the occupants of the long house moved to their summer wigwams to take advantage of the warmer weather. During the summer, the cooking was done outside in front of the individual wigwams.

The island was the length of the flight of a brave's arrow and about half as wide. Its elevated knolls stood some 20 feet above the surface of the lake. The island was covered with a variety of trees including pine, hemlock, birch, maple, oak, and ash. Its shores were lined with alders in which were mixed many blueberry bushes. There were no low-lying swampy areas where stagnant water would breed mosquitoes so the island was remarkably free of insects during the summer. The few mosquitoes encountered were blown across the channel from the mainland. Small smudges were sometimes burned at the entrance of the tent at night to deter insects. The Indians sometimes used insecticides such as garlic as a repellent.

Metaxta, like most squaws, kept a low fire in the hearth going all the time. There was generally a clay pot of stew set close to the fire for a hungry child or husband and for the occasional visitor. Indians tended to eat when they were hungry, but in the summer, when women worked the garden, it was customary to have one large meal.

Metaxta began to prepare the partridge. One of the braves had also brought them a large bass which had been taken from a canoe using drop lines and shiners for bait. She cut the head off the bird, stuffed the stomach cavity with wild garlic and other seasonings. She now plucked out the long wing and tail feathers and bound the wings and legs tightly to the body with twine made from inside bark fibers. This is made by stripping off the wet inner bark and rolling on the thigh to form a flexible twine.

She had a supply of a special clay that was also used for making pottery which she now worked to the right consistency with water until it was pliable like soft molding clay. She coated the entire bird with a two-inch covering making sure that there were no openings. Now, after cleaning the large fish, she encased it in its own clay coating. Opening a space in the coals, she placed the bird and the fish directly on the coals and covered them both with glowing embers from the fire.

She now went to her birch-bark container and poured out some finely ground maize into a hand-carved wooden bowl. Adding water she worked it to a stiff consistency which she formed into an eight-inch wheel about two inches thick. When finished to her satisfaction, she dipped her hand in water and carefully smoothed the surface. The corn bread wheel was formed on some wide green leaves which she now folded over the top until completely covered. Now she moved to the fire, prepared a space in the white ashes and slid the cake directly onto the coals. Carefully heaping hot white ashes over the top of the leaves, she sat back to tend her fire.

By the time she removed her meal, the bird and fish had cooked in the fire for almost an hour and the cornbread less than 20 minutes. She broke the brittle clay covering the bird and the fish. Most of the feathers and fish skin came away with the baked clay. Out from the charred leaves came the corn bread fully baked and they were ready to begin their meal. They ate from carved wooden plates which were personal possessions that each person guarded carefully. Their utensils were the short steel knife with wooden handle they carried in a hide case suspended from their necks by a thong. In place of a fork they used an eating awl which was like a pick for spearing food. Each individual had a large wooden spoon he used to eat the stew which was most commonly served.[3]

The Chief ate eagerly, displaying his pleasure the Indian way, with frequent grunts of appreciation and exclamations about how good the meal was. His wife listened stoically having been long accustomed to these comments.

They had eaten as all Indians ate--sitting on the ground, legs crossed, with their plates on their lap. Each person was responsible for his own eating utensils. If an Indian brave wanted to eat from clean plates and with clean utensils it was his responsibility to wash and take care of his own eating equipment. This practice was drilled into Indian children at a very young age.

After the sun set, the men of the tribe began to come by for their regular evening smoke around the Chief's camp-fire. The conversation turned to the events of the day as to who caught the fish and what was used for bait.

The lookouts spoke of seeing smoke to the south, but they did not know the reason for the smoke. The Chief assigned two braves to scout in the direction of the smoke the following day to learn if there was any threat to the

---

[3] The Indian How Book, Arthur C. Parker, (p.189-194) Describes Indian cooking methods and eating utensils.

tribe. The conversation turned to the salmon and shad run the previous month at the Amoskeag Falls.

For centuries the Abenaki Indians converged on the Merrimac River in May for the annual spawning run of salmon, shad and smelt. The shad and salmon arrived at the Falls near the Pawtucket Tribe in Lowell the first week in May. By May 15, the run began at the falls of the Amosgeag Tribe of Manchester and by the end of May it had arrived at Lake Winnipesaukee. At the fork of the Merrimac River north of Franklin, the shad continued up to Winnipesaukee and the salmon went up the Pemigewasett.

For as long as anyone in the tribe could remember, they camped in Lowell for the spawning run with the permission of the Pawtucket Tribe; but now, as the colonists pushed up the river, they were forced to move up to the Amoskeag Falls for the fish run. There, the entire tribe--men, women and children--camped while the men speared and netted salmon, shad and smelt. They gorged themselves on fresh fish and kept fires going constantly to dry the fish on hardwood racks built above the fires. The dried fish were carried back to their village on Escumbuit Island, where they were stored in bark containers placed in holes in the ground covered by bark to keep out the elements. This store of dried fish lasted through the winter until the ice left the lake.

Escumbuit was elected the Civil Chief of this small, isolated band of Indians, driven from their ancestral home in Massachusetts by the encroaching English settlers. The Civil Chief was like the mayor of a small town, responsible for the general welfare of the tribe and normally acting as their spokesman in matters affecting the tribe. If they went on the war-path, the tribe would elect a War Chief--chosen for his past exploits in battle. His cunning, daring, fearlessness and ruthlessness would earn him the right to this position.

Chief Escumbuit was a famous War Chief and Sachem of the fierce Pigwacket Indians from the north. Now, in comparative obscurity, his past glories earned him the respect of the members of this small band and they looked up to him. Sadly, due to his injury, and now his age, he would never lead braves on the war-path again.

They knew only that he was forced to leave his tribe because he killed one brave and wounded another in a personal dispute. His reputation as a warrior and his exploits against the English outweighed any concern they had for a distant tribal dispute. They were content to have such a famous Indian as part of their tribe.

The conversation around the fireplace turned to the coming seasonal migration to the sea coast. The state of the crops that were planted--and now being cared for by the women of the tribe--determined when they would be ready to make their annual move to the coast. The conversation was animated and upbeat because the Indians looked forward to their summer by the ocean. The warm months of June, July and August were the only months in the Indian calendar when they did not have to scratch desperately to subsist.

The ancient site of their summer camp now known as Seabrook and Hampton was no longer safe for them. The steady pressure of the English forced the Indians to move northward in their summer food search. So the men talked about the logistics of their planned move to the area now called Great Bay. Like any person planning to go away for several months, they decided what they needed to take with them and how they were to transport this equipment to the new location.

Since their canoes were essential for their livelihood at Great Bay, they discussed who would man the canoes and what equipment to carry in them. Taking the canoes down the Spicket River required many portages past shallows and beaver dams. Once they reached the Merrimac, the journey down stream to the ocean was simple. The 80-pound canoes, even loaded with the rolled-up bark covering of the wigwams, did not require much water. In many places the braves simply waded in the stream bed pushing the canoes ahead of them. Once they reached the ocean, they only waited for good weather to paddle north to Kittery where they paddled up the river with the incoming tide to join the rest of the tribe at their summer camp. The canoes were essential to the tribe during their stay at the seashore. The remaining squaws and children, together with armed braves, traveled over ancient Indian trails to Great Bay. They followed the Pawtucket trail to Sandown where they headed west on the Swanscott trail through Exeter and Stratford to the south shore of Great Bay.

Once a date was agreed upon, the braves gradually drifted back to their individual wigwams to carry the good news of the departure for their camp.

This was a big yearly event for the women. Life at the seashore offered a welcome break from the continuous grind of work on their island home. The men went out in the canoes fishing, spearing lobsters and shooting seals, while the women gathered clams and oysters and cooked the wonderful bounty of the sea. It was a time for relaxation for everyone.

When the last brave left his fire, Escumbuit knocked the spent ashes from his pipe, refilling it with the mixture of tobacco, sumac leaves and alder bark the Indians called *kinnikinnik*. Using the lit end of a pine twig to re-light his pipe, he leaned back against the giant pine, drawing several deep drafts on the pipe until it glowed in the darkness. As he sat in silence, looking into the depths of the fire, his troubled thoughts turned to the small settlement of paleface which now occupied part of their hunting grounds to the immediate north.

They came with their wives and children during a period of peace in the unending series of wars with the English. Six uneasy winters passed and there were no conflicts between the two tribes, in spite of the strange customs of the paleface. They sailed up the river to Haverhill in their great ship and their men explored the country to the north, deciding to settle their people in an area they called Nutfield. Even before they built their own lodges they built a longhouse in which they prayed to their Great Spirit whom they called God.

The Chief mused to himself: "In the time of my raids with the French their scalps would be hung on the pole of my wigwam, but now, our father in Canada tells me these people are different from the English we have always fought. Also, it is just this year that our leaders have signed a peace treaty with the English ending our three year war with their Governor Dummer. We leave them in peace to plant their strange crops. One is the root they call the potato which my people tell me fills the stomach and is good to eat. The other is the strange plants from which their men and their women weave a fine cloth they call linen.[4] Is it possible that we can live in peace with these strange people whose language sounds different than the English? If they wish to live in peace with us, why did they build their two lodges with holes from which to fire their muskets; and who is it they do not trust? My people still harvest the butternuts, the walnuts and chestnuts from the lands they occupy with no complaint from these pale-face, but are my people too trusting? My people have not suffered the treachery of the paleface that Escumbuit has seen--they trust too much; their Chief must keep his vigil!

"How simple are my people. Except for the old, none have known the feel of a war club crushing the head of the enemy. Their ears have not heard the howl of the warrior in battle, the keen of his scalping cry as he takes a scalp in battle, the crash of the cannon, and the cries of the wounded. They know nothing of the wonders of people across the great water--the great palaces--carriages with wheels pulled by horses. They know *nothing* of these things! When I speak of such wonders they are silent and their eyes tell me they do not believe.

---

[4] From Turnpike To Interstate, Derry Historical Society, 1827-1977, Scotch/Irish immigrants, seeking religious freedom settled in Nutfield (Derry) in 1719. Their minister, the Reverend James MacGregor, and the Governor of Canada, the Marquis Vaudreuil, were college classmates. Vaudreuil issued orders, through resident Jesuit missionaries to the Abenaki Indians, to desist from attacks on the village, declaring that these people were "different" than the English whom the Indians had been fighting for years. In the wars which came after Nutfield was settled, namely, Dummer's War With The Eastern Abenakis, 1722-1725; King George's War(War Of The Spanish Succession), 1740-1748; The French and Indian War(Seven Years War),1755-1763, the village of Derry, New Hampshire was never attacked.

"How did I, the greatest Pigwacket Chief and Sachem, end up so?"

How did it begin and how will it end? With that, he rose, knocked the dead ashes of the *kinnikinnick* from his pipe, limped to his wigwam, lay down on his low pallet and soon fell asleep.

Signed Sealed and delivered
in the preſence of us,

Edmund Quinſey
Spencer Phips
Wil. Dudley
Shad. Walton
Joſiah Willard
&c.

Signum *Kirebenuit*

Signum *Warraeenſitt*

Signum *Bomaſeen*

Signum *Wadacanaquin*

Signum *Æneas*

Signum *Iteanſis*

Signum *Jackoid*

Signum *Joſeph*

Indian Totems.

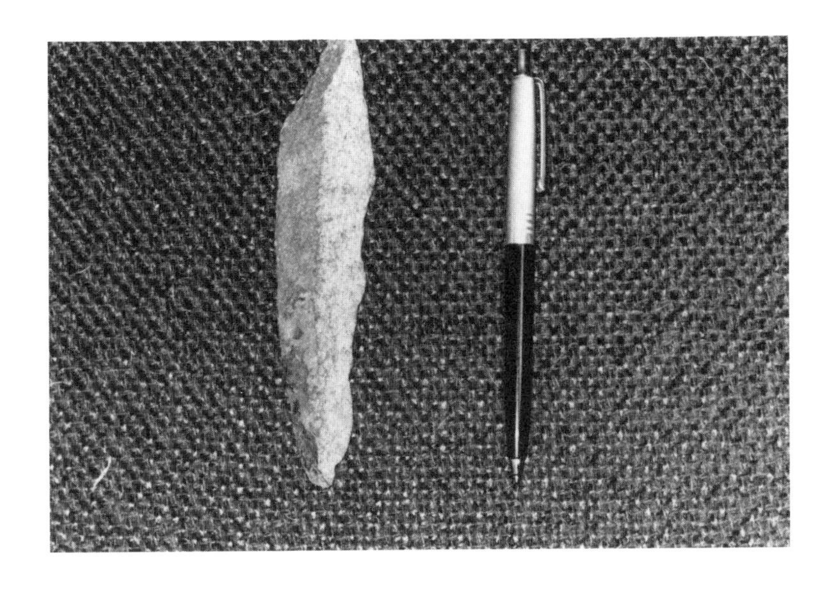

Top: Stone knife. Bottom: Amoskeag Falls

ESCUMBUIT'S YOUTH
1665-1693

For generations before the coming of the white man, the beautiful valley of the upper Saco River had been the home of the Pigwacket Indians. The name Pigwacket resembles certain root words of the Algonquin language and appears to describe the sweeping turns of the river as it passes close by the large beautiful sheet of water now know as Lovewell Pond.

The valley, attended by the White Mountains to the west, abounded in wild-life. Moose, deer, elk, bears, wolves, beaver and fish were plentiful. The un-forested intervals of the valley provided fertile land for the primitive agriculture of the Indians. Here they planted their corn, pumpkins, beans, squash and tobacco.

The heart of Pigwacket country was that section of the valley now occupied by the towns of Fryeburg, Maine, and Conway and Bartlett in New Hampshire.

When Chief Escumbuit was a youth, his village had 250 bark wigwams and a large stockade fort. The area was home to 1,500 to 2,000 Indians. The white-man-carried epidemic of 1617 wiped out so many thousands of northeast Indians that the survivors were unable to bury the dead. This event, and the following relentless encroachment of the white man, signaled their doom.

The river was a powerful provider of the Indians' necessities. Besides its teeming fish, it attracted a multitude of fur-bearing animals. It was a highway which enabled them to travel north into the White Mountains on hunting forays and southeast to the seacoast where riches of oysters, clams, lobster, seal, porpoise and fish awaited.

Chief Escumbuit was born into this aboriginal culture in 1665. Some articles such as hatchets, hoes, metal pots and muskets had been obtained from traders on the coast in exchange for beaver furs, but the Indians lacked the knowledge of making cloth fabrics by weaving the wool fibers of domesticated animals.

The primitive culture into which he was born had very simple standards. They believed in the immortality of the soul. From the dim mists of their history was handed down the story of a great deluge. A single man and woman survived this deluge on a mountain top. From this couple emerged the people of the world.

Their code of conduct was simple, but rigorous. The Spartan virtues--to speak the truth, to scorn fear and exalt valor, to endure and to repay in kind good for good and evil for evil--these were the mark of a man and warrior. Like many so-called civilized people, the Pigwacket Indians were ruthless with their enemies and the torture of their captives could be ingenious. The treatment of their captives could be cruel, but invariably they held inviolate the chastity of women. They shared a deeply-held belief of good and bad spirits and believed that all things, both living and inanimate, were living things. Their great mythical spirit was Gluskap, whom the Indians believed to be capable of prodigious feats and who was a great teacher and hero. He taught them how to inhabit the earth and how they should live, about spiritual power and how to fight the forces and overcome the obstacles that are against the nature of mankind. They feared a bird-like creature named Pomola, which lived on the summit of Katahdin, the highest mountain in Maine, where they feared to travel. They appeased evil spirits and gave mythical powers to the good.

The Pigwacket tribe was but one of the many local tribes which were part of the Abenaki Indians living in Maine and New Hampshire. Historians describe the Indians of Maine as the Eastern Abenaki Indians, while those of New Hampshire were called the Western Abenaki. The Indian translation for Abenaki is "People at the Dawn."

As the sun rose in the east over the rim of the Atlantic Ocean, it shone first on the Abenakis of Maine and New Hampshire; hence, the derivation of the name "Dawn People."

The names of the tribes generally described the area where they lived. Thus, the Amoskeag Indians of Manchester meant "place of fish traps"; Pawtucket Indians of Lowell meant "at the falls in the tidal river." The Algonquian language spoken by these tribes had no written alphabet and was a language of images instead of ideas. It was spoken in a low monotone and has been described as "so soft and fluttery as to not disturb even the birds."

The son of obscure parents, as a child Escumbuit was known as "Ottucke," the Indian name for deer, apparently earning this nickname because of his exceptional running ability. Soon after birth, his father was killed by a raiding party of Iroquois, who lived to the west in the area we now know as upper New York State. For centuries, the Iroquois were the mortal enemies of the Abenaki Indians. The cruelty of the Pigwacket Indians was exceeded only by that of the Iroquois of the Hudson Valley.

Before the arrival of the white man, the Abenaki tribes of New Hampshire and Maine were compelled to join forces to resist the incursions into their territory by the war-like Iroquois. Otherwise, before the arrival of the white man, they had engaged in petty inter-tribal vendettas among the New England tribes. Poaching on tribal hunting territory or disputes over favored fish spearing sites during the spring run of the shad and salmon usually led to inter-tribal conflict, resulting in raids by small bands of braves against neighboring tribes in which a member of the offending tribe might be killed and a child or a squaw abducted and forced to become a member of the raiding tribe.

There was a serious flaw in the teaching and culture of the Indians. Children from an early age were drilled in the Spartan code which demanded, "You must learn to endure the hardships of extreme cold, hunger, pain and adversity. To prove you are a man, you must kill one of our enemy or at least smoke the hibernating bear from his cave and kill him face to face with your war club. Then you have earned the right to take a young woman of our tribe as your wife."

Later, when the tribe elders were counseling peace in their dealing with the paleface, they had difficulty restraining their 15 and 16-year old braves who, fired by the rum of unscrupulous English traders, wanted only to take English scalps.

Ottucke was raised by his mother and uncle who were worried by his seeming inability to get along with the other children. Sullen and uncommunicative, he was first picked on by the other children. Although he was bigger than his counterparts, he was the butt of their ridicule and jokes. His most prized possession was a small flint dagger given to him by his uncle which he carried in a deerskin pouch hung from his neck on a rawhide thong.

One day he left it safely in its pouch on the shore of the lake while he and the other boys went swimming. In the water, he suddenly looked up to see one of the boys on shore holding his dagger aloft over a dead log on the shore shouting, "Die, you Iroquois dog! I will now take your scalp." With that he plunged the dagger into the log and the blade of the brittle flint knife snapped leaving the point buried in the log.

In a blind fury the young Ottucke surged to the shore, threw himself at the offending boy and, with immense strength, turned him face down and began to pound his face onto the log. The efforts of the other children to pull him off the boy were futile. Only the intervention of two adult squaws kept him from beating the 10 year old to death. From that moment, his reputation as a warrior began to grow.

As a child learns that his tantrums bring results, the young brave immediately sensed that he could now dominate his play-mates. From then on, he was ruthless with them. He never forgot their earlier treatment of him. In their games of lacrosse, he was always one of the two captains, and the other children vied to be on his team so they would not have to be on the receiving end of his vicious racket.

In their winter game of *snow snake* in which they competed to see who could propel the blunt ended stick the furthest along the channel in the snow, he always won.

Like a missile that has been launched and cannot be recalled, he thrived on his new-found power. Only he could bend and string the bow that his uncle made for him. He demonstrated his ability to kill rabbits and squirrels at ranges that his companions would not even attempt. Now he had no challengers, for they feared him. Secretly they didn't like him, but like subservient wolves in the wolf-pack hierarchy, they were forced to submit and follow.

When he was 14 years old, his uncle took him aside and told him that the time had come for him to go on his *vision quest* in search of his *Manatou*. Indian youths, at puberty, went to an isolated spot where they might spend days waiting for a vision to appear of the animal they would take as their life-long guardian and advisor. This could be an animal, a fish, or a bird and the owner learned to draw a crude outline of his totem which he would draw as a signature on documents. Also, in a raid on the enemy, he might draw his *totem* on a dead body or on a nearby object where it would prove it was he who had taken this terrible revenge.

Ottucke took his canoe up the Saco to a secret cave that only he knew. There, he remained alone, hungry and cold, but determined to stay until his vision appeared. Finally, in the early dark of the third night, hungry, weak and in despair, he looked up at the moon from the opening of his cave and began to talk directly to the spirits of his ancestors:

Oh great spirits, hear my call,
My soul seeks your great wisdom,
My thoughts are only of you,
And the Manatou you prepare for me.
Great Manatou, protect me from life's harm!
Hear me! and let me see your form,

That I might know you and obey you,
For this I pledge you my life!
My soul is yours, my Manatou,
Set my life course, open my eyes wide,
So my destiny will be revealed to me.

Weak from hunger, and almost in a trance from his long ordeal, he sat at the mouth of his cave in the growing darkness, waiting for a sign. In the waning light and shadows cast by the overhanging cliff, he suddenly saw it! There it was--unmistakable in its form--the outspread wings, the outspread talons--the arched head with its cruel beak--a magnificent eagle!

"Oh! great Manatou, at last you have heeded my call. I feared you might not reveal yourself to me. I was afraid to go to my uncle and tell him that my Manatou had not shown himself to me. Now I am no longer afraid. Now I can return to my village and tell them the mighty eagle is the guardian of my destiny. It is to you I will pray when I need guidance, you, my totem for life, will be proud of my deeds."

By now, it was fully dark and the boy eagerly went to the river for his canoe. With a feeling of tremendous relief and a sense of euphoria, the tired boy, fueled by the rush of adrenaline, pushed off in his canoe and paddled through the darkness towards his village.[5]

As winter approached in that same year, Ottucke spent as much time as he could with his uncle. When the deep snow came, the women and children moved into the long-

---

[5] The Indian How Book, Arthur c. Parker (p.229-31) Describes the general theme of Indian youths going on their vision quest.

house inside the palisade while the men and young braves prepared for the winter hunt. They knew where the deer and moose wintered and they waited for the deep snow to arrive which they knew would hamper the mobility of their prey. Muskets, powder and ball were still rare in the tribe and the men counted on the age old practice of running down the deer and moose on snow shoes. The animals, exhausted from trying to run through snow three and four foot deep, were finally easy prey for a savage assault with spear and dagger. The carcasses of the animals were dragged back to the village on toboggans pulled by the braves.

Almost every part of the game was used by the Indians. The meat that wasn't consumed fresh was cut off in strips, smoked and dried over their fires. Moose hide was particularly suited for winter moccasins. They were often worn over inner deer-skin moccasins and could be made almost completely water-proof. Certain sinew of both the deer and moose were cut out and saved and were used to sew the seams of the fine buck-skin shirts and leggings made from the deer hides. Even the hooves were saved and used to make a strong glue.

Ottucke, who would not be 15 years old until the following spring, was immensely proud of being named a member of his uncle's ten man team. Once on the hunt, he proved himself equal to any of the mature men. He seemed to glide over the snow in his ash and raw-hide snow shoes. When the moose began their vain attempt to put distance between themselves and the braves, it was he who ranged ahead of the others and brought down the first moose with his spear. Seeming to disregard the flailing antlers and hooves, he leaped on the back of the animal, the dagger in his right hand, rising and falling in a series of fatal wounds to the doomed animal. Finally, he stood over his dying prey and then, with bloody arms raised high, uttered the blood-curdling war cry of the Pigwacket Indian.

By the time the small band dragged the loaded toboggans back to the village, Ottucke had earned his reputation with the other men. They no longer tried to frighten him with their stories of the dangers of the hunt. By now, they knew that this young Pigwacket feared nothing. Also, they had seen him handle the 20 below zero temperatures and the other hardships of the hunt without complaint. The gossip in the village was of the young boy-warrior with the skill and bravery of a chief--and not yet 15.

The previous spring a war party of Iroquois from the Hudson Valley had surprised a small group of Indians engaged in tapping a grove of maple trees for syrup. The Iroquois party of about 25 warriors had lay hidden for some time to make sure that they were safe from counter attack from the main village. They descended upon the Pigwacket group en masse killing and taking the scalps of the four adult males at once. One woman resisted and was killed and scalped after which the Iroquois made a rapid withdrawal herding the two remaining squaws and three children ahead of them.

When the group failed to return to the village that night, searchers to the maple grove came upon the grim results of the lightning attack. By the time a party was organized to pursue the Iroquois, their lead was too great. They tracked them to the Connecticut river where they lost their trail on the west bank. Having no idea whether they had gone north or south, the Pigwackets were forced to give up the chase.

Their Indian code demanded revenge and the form and extent of the reprisal was discussed in long meetings at the Chief's council. As always, the younger braves were for an immediate attack on the Iroquois in their own country. The elders argued that an impetuous attack would be anticipated by the enemy giving them the opportunity to set up an ambush. Wisdom finally prevailed, but the insult to the tribe had been festering in the minds of its members ever since. Now, a year later, every member of the tribe thirsted for revenge: The Iroquois must pay!

The Chief's Council decided to send a war party of 20 braves split into two units with an experienced brave leading each unit. A single chief was selected to lead the entire group. The Indians did not designate generals, captains, sergeants and lieutenants in their fighting units. Each group of ten warriors chose a brave who had proven his courage and ability to lead them. If he did not display sufficient valor and ferocity, he would be replaced by another brave eager to build his reputation.

It was not surprising that three quarters of the party were young braves in the 15 to 18 year age group. The customs of the tribe placed tremendous pressure on these young braves to prove themselves and to be accepted as full fledged members of the tribe. The approval of their elders to marry might depend on their participation and performance during this raid. What was surprising was that the 15-year old Ottucke was chosen among the many volunteers. He was bigger, faster and stronger than many of the other young braves. More than that, however, his quiet intensity and the fury of his temper was already well known in the tribe. Other braves, young and old, avoided provoking him.

The customary *powwow* was held to get the warriors in the proper fighting mood. There was the usual dancing and chanting accompanied by the tom tom. There were speeches by various members of the tribe including the women. Even the resident French Jesuit priest from Canada gave his blessing to the war party and led the prayers of the villagers as many of the women said their beads. Finally the war party filed into the woods as the entire village watched.

The warriors traveled very light as they followed the Kancamagus trail over to the area of Holderness. Each man had his bow and quiver of arrows together with a war club or a tomahawk slung from a loop at the waist. In a pouch suspended from the neck they carried fire making equipment and a supply of tobacco for the ever present pipe. By now, most men carried short steel daggers obtained from either English or French traders. Muskets were still scarce and not practical for the stealthy hit and run attack the party planned. In deer-skin bags slung on their backs, they carried a basic ration of parched corn and a supply of pemmican to be used in an emergency. Pemmican consisted of a high energy mixture of animal grease, dried meat, nuts and dried berries. When there was no time to hunt for game, or if they were in a hurry, they could subsist on the pemmican and the parched corn.

They switched to the Asquamchumaukee trail near Holderness which took them to the Connecticut River, at which point they followed the river south via the Kwanitegok until they arrived just south of Claremont.[6]

---

[6] Historic Indian Trails of New Hampshire, Chester B. Price, 1974. New England was cris-crossed by well-known Indian trails which today are the route of some of our major highways. Many of the lesser trails have become hiking trails, bicycle and bridal paths.

South of Claremont, the war party headed west where they would traverse the Green Mountains in the Manchester area. Now they were very close to their objective--the Hudson River south of Glens Falls. They were in no hurry. They hunted on the way, killing small game and even stopping to fish in some of the streams. When they got into Iroquois country, they avoided the obvious trails using a two man advance team to scout ahead for the enemy. When they reached the Hudson, they chose a densely wooded spot for a base from which they could reconnoiter the enemy.

The river was heavily traveled by the Iroquois in their canoes. On the east shore, about a mile from their base camp, they found a spot where a small brook discharged its water into the Hudson. Its banks were steep and afforded excellent cover close to a small sandbar left by the spring freshets. Two days of careful study by the Chief and his two lieutenants confirmed that this was a favorite spot for travelers to stop and take a break from their canoes. Small groups stopped here to cook a hot meal or take a swim and even pass the night before resuming their journey. Best of all, it was secluded and a long way from the Indian village at Glens Falls.

The Chief and his two leaders agreed that they had found an ideal site for a classic Indian ambush. A nighttime strike on a sleeping party was rejected for fear that

---

These trails, centuries old, were first made by animals of the forest going to water, or in search of smaller prey attracted by the water. The Indians adapted these animal traits and the white man has followed suit to a large degree.

some of the victims could make the cover of the woods in the darkness and spread the alarm. They agreed that except for the captives they chose to take with them, all others had to be killed and scalped. There would be no time to torture in the Iroquois way. They hoped to be back in the Green Mountains with their captives before they were discovered.

The day of the planned attack, the Chief had them all wash themselves using a strong soap made from wood ashes and animal fat. They then rubbed their arm pits and groin area with sweet ferns taken from the woods. Even though the prey was man, the Chief followed the ritual of the hunt. He wanted no man odor betraying their presence to the enemy. The men spent their time reclining waiting the signal from the look-out posted at the outlet to the river.

By late afternoon the adrenaline of the braves had begun to ebb as it seemed as though the day had been wasted. Suddenly the look-out came up the brook and excitedly told of four canoes coming up-stream from far down the river, but close to shore. In about 20 minutes the agreed signals in the form of bird cries began to filter back to the group. Five canoes: five male stern-paddlers, three male and two squaw bow-paddlers, and twelve passengers of squaws and children. Now, the agonizing question: will they land?

The final signal had the effect of a musket shot to the men: "They are coming ashore!"

Now, every brave to his assigned spot, his heart pounding in his chest, his bow already strung, his first arrow notched, his war club at his feet, his dagger in his belt, his nerves as tight as the string of his bow.

Now they are coming up the brook: the laughter of the children, the chatter of the squaws, an adult command!

The bow of the first canoe appears followed by the rest. The canoe lands on the sand bar, the lead brave steps out and pulls the canoe up on the sand. "Wait! Heed the warning of the Chief. You must wait until the first two canoes have landed. Then I will give the signal."

Ottucke already had his bow drawn, his aim on his assigned target. Finally it came--the simple call of the chick-a-dee. His Iroquois turned to face him just as his arrow buried itself in his chest. A maelstrom of sound ruptured the silence of the peaceful brook--Pigwacket war cries, capsized canoes, screams of the Iroquois and mass panic.

Out of this hellish scene and somehow unscathed in the first volley of arrows, straight at Ottucke ran a young muscular brave, tomahawk in hand, screaming his defiance. Ottucke dropped his bow, snatched his war club and rose to meet the charge. The Iroquois attacked, slashing the fleshy part of his left shoulder as Escumbuit evaded to the right. Swinging sideward, he caught the Iroquois a glancing blow to the side of his head as the momentum of his charge carried him to his knees. He whirled instantly, but it was too late. Escumbuit was on him like a mountain lion, smashing his head with his war club as if it were a rotten pumpkin in the field.

Knowing instantly that the Iroquois was dead, he now charged for the brook, his murderous instincts unleashed. By the time he got there, the slaughter had been completed by the others. As the squaws and the children were being herded onto the sand bar, heated arguments broke out over the rightful owners of the scalps. This would be decided by individual marks on each arrow identifying its owner.

Ottucke turned his Iroquois victim over, took out his knife and made a circular cut around the circumference of the head. Pulling on the Iroquois scalp lock, he peeled and cut the scalp away from the skull. Dipping his finger in the blood of the dead Iroquois, he then carefully drew the crude outline of an eagle on the dead brave's torso--*his* totem, that of *his* Manatou. Now, returning to the body of the young brave who had charged him, he repeated the procedure. He felt a slight wave of admiration for the bravery of the dead youth, but no regrets, only euphoria. He was a Pigwacket warrior fulfilling his destiny.

After inspecting the women and children survivors, the Chief and his two lieutenants had a short discussion. They selected two healthy squaws plus one boy and two young girls. These were led off to begin the long trip home. Once out of sight, they turned to complete their revenge. They killed two babies and the remaining squaws who were either too young or too old to keep up with the Pigwackets on their way home.

The entire ambush and clean-up had lasted about 20 minutes. With luck it could be a whole day before their deed was discovered by a chance band of Iroquois. Now they must make all possible speed toward their own territory. The captives would be told that they must match the pace of the war party lest the tomahawk would fall and only their scalp would reach the village of the Pigwacket.

They traveled eastward the rest of the day and throughout the night with the captives tethered to their captors by lengths of rawhide. Each warrior had extra moose hide moccasins to replace those worn out on the trails. They had additional moccasins for the captives. After they crossed the Connecticut River into New Hampshire, they removed the restraints, but carefully trussed each prisoner when they stopped to sleep. The squaws were not molested in any way. Perhaps the knowledge that any of these captives could end up a sister or relative in their own family had a restraining influence on the braves. As for the captives, they endured their ordeal stoically in the Indian fashion. The men killed small game as they traveled east. Squirrels, rabbits and hare were plentiful. When at last they felt safe from pursuit, they lit small smokeless campfires, stopping to broil the small game on green sticks.

On the morning of the final day's march to their village, the Chief took Ottucke and a young brave named *Moosu* aside, saying, "Run to our village and tell our people that the war party returns with Iroquois captives and scalps. When they ask questions, tell them they must wait for the arrival of the chief. Their Chief will tell them the story of our victory over the Iroquois at the celebration tonight."

The arrival of Ottucke and Moosu in the village created great excitement, especially when they saw the two Iroquois scalps hanging from Ottucke's belt. Women were recalled from work in the tribal gardens and preparations for a giant celebration began. When the war party entered the village, everyone had turned out to greet their heroes and to inspect the captives. The captives were not molested, but had been told that the following day they would have to run the gauntlet. That night they were on display as the warriors sang and danced their scalp dance to the beat of tom toms.

The Indian gauntlet has been described as little more than a ritual which posed no real threat to its victims. Other historians claim that people were seriously injured and sometimes killed running the gauntlet. It can be assumed that it depended upon the crowd psychology of the tormentors at the moment as well as the nature of the victims. That is to say, were the victims mature fighting men, women, or children? It appears that the practice was a type of rough sport or entertainment for the participants and also a method of testing the mettle of the captives.

Two lines of Indians armed with switches, clubs and pointed sticks were lined up about four paces apart. This provided a space about 12 feet wide. At the far end of the two lines a post was buried in the ground; close by, a small wigwam or shelter was erected. The victims were stripped and forced to run between the two lines as the Indians attempted to whip them, hit them with clubs, trip them, or stab them with spears. The tormentors had to stay behind the line. When a victim reached the post, he or she was safe and led to the small shelter to rest and have the wounds tended.

There is one recorded incident where an English soldier running the gauntlet knocked down an Indian at the beginning of the line, snatched his club and beat his way through the gauntlet injuring several of the Indians. On this occasion there was a great deal of merriment and ridicule of the Indians who had been bested. The bravery and skill of the soldier was applauded and his life spared.

In this case, the two Iroquois squaws would run a gauntlet made up of women of the village, and the children, likewise, would be tested by Pigwacket children. After being tested in this manner, the Chief's Council would hear petitions from the various families who wished to adopt one of the captives into their own family. It was possible that these captives could be adopted by relatives of the victims of the Iroquois raid the previous year.

Into this Stone Age culture, which celebrated man's inhumanity to man, was added the additional ingredient of war between two great European powers. The war between England and France over the fur trade and territorial rights extended from the frontier villages of the English Colonists up into Newfoundland and into the upper Hudson Valley and along the Canadian frontier into the Great Lakes. Both sides used Indian allies to fight their battles for them. The English Colonists used their centuries old diplomatic skills to exploit the ancient rivalries between the southern New England tribes. By this time they had subdued Indian resistance in Massachusetts. Metacomen, the Wampenaug Chief known as King Philip, had been killed and his tribe wiped out, ending the King Philip War in 1677.

The earliest French contact with the Pigwacket Indians was in 1642. In 1651, the Jesuit Father Gabriel Druillettes formed an alliance of the Penacooks, Pocumtucks, Mahicans and the Sokokis to join the French in a solid front against the Iroquois. From their trading post in Albany, New York, the English used the fierce Iroquois as a buffer between themselves and the French in Canada, who were competing with them for the fur trade.

As the battle for control of the area from Newfoundland down to the Kennebec in Maine heated up, King Louis XIV of France gave strict orders to the Canadians to avoid provoking the Iroquois in New York because he didn't want to fight the English on two fronts. The colonists were pushing their settlements up the rivers of Maine and New Hampshire and his priority was on forcing them back to their Massachusetts base.

The war between the French and the English became a religious war as well as a war over the fur trade and fishing rights in Newfoundland. Jesuit missionaries were sent to the major Indian settlements initially to convert the savages to Catholicism. By 1688, the Jesuits had a dual mission. One cannot question their dedication to convert the Indians, but they had taken on the additional political role of inciting the Indians against the English. They were remarkably successful in both endeavors, partly due to the care with which they had been selected for the service, and partly due to their willingness to live among the Indians and learn their language and customs.

The clergy of the English colonists was also interested in converting the savages, but the people they sent to do the job were generally ill-suited for the work. They established some Indian churches, but they used interpreters to preach to the Indians and their Puritanical style of worship failed to impress the Indians. In contrast to the Jesuits, they chose to live apart from the Indians and made no effort to learn their language or share their customs.

The French Historian Charlevoix wrote, "Religion is the chief bond by which the savage is attached to us." Another critic of the period wrote, "While Humanity is in the savage state, it can only be Christianized on the surface; and the convert of the Jesuits remained a savage still. They did not even try to civilize him. They taught him to repeat a catechism which he could not understand, and practice rites which were incomprehensible to him. To his eyes the crucifix was a fetish of surpassing power and the Mass a beneficent "medicine" or occult influence. Yet he would not forget his old rooted beliefs, and it needed the constant presence of the missionary to prevent him from returning to them."

Another French historian, in response to the frequent bitter complaints by English historians about the French failure to prevent the atrocities of their Indian allies, commented, "Remember, these English are the same people who were burning women at the stake for witchcraft in Boston and where common criminals were cut asunder and thrown to the elements without burial."

(It becomes apparent that things never change. Your understanding of the Jewish/Arab enmity depends on whether you get the story from a Jew or an Arab. This applies equally to the Serbians and Bosnians. It seems safe to predict that the world will always have conflicts so long as men and their frailties are involved. You can find apologists for each of the combatants in this seventeenth and eighteenth century drama. One has to wonder if the white man had not appeared on this continent, would not the Indians exist today as in the previous ten thousand years?)

The colonial wars have been recorded in hundreds of historical books written by both French and English historians. The litany of political ambition, treachery, treaties and broken treaties seems endless. In these circumstances, where we are trying to trace the rise and fall of one Indian in this greater human panorama, it is sufficient to list the various wars without going into detail as to their cause and their outcome. From the Indian point of view, it must have seemed like one long war which lasted almost 100 years.

- 1675--1677 King Phillip's War. The war of the English Colonists with the Wampenaug Indians of Massachusetts led by Chief Metacomen.

- 1675--1697 King William's War
- 1702--1713 Queen Ann's War (War of the Spanish Succession)
- 1722--1725 Governor Dummer's War with the Eastern Abenaki Indians
- 1740--1748 King George's War (War of the Austrian Succession)
- 1755--1763 French and Indian War (The Seven Years War)

There were periods between the major wars when the English and the Indians traded with each other or faced each other over the negotiating table. When fighting broke out anew, each side would often know the names of the commanders leading the opposing forces. Historical accounts written by the English often mis-spell the names of the French commanders and fail to identify individual Indian warriors. By reading the French account of these same actions, however, it is possible to correctly name not only the Frenchmen involved, but to identify the Indian leaders who fought with them.

After the Iroquois raid, young Ottucke basked in the admiration of his fellow tribesmen, and the experience did wonders for his general demeanor. As his confidence grew, his circle of friends increased and he began to enjoy himself more. A young girl of the tribe had caught his eye and, by Indian standards, he had proved himself a man qualified to take a bride.

He and his friend Moosu had gone on a hunt in which they had stalked and killed a deer. Now Ottucke went to his uncle and asked him to speak to the parents of the girl on his behalf. The deer was an offering to the parents of the girl, but there was more. He had taken a small, carved soapstone amulet from the body of one of the Iroquois he had slain. This crude figure of a turtle had been worn about the neck of the dead warrior, suspended by a length of raw-hide, and was his present to the girl, *Atchitamon*, the Algonquin for head first like the chipmunk.

The Uncle did his job well and the parents agreed to a trial marriage. Ottucke moved into the wigwam of the girl's parents where they slept head to toe for one week. At the end of the week, after observing the couple together, the parents judged them to be ready for a formal marriage which was celebrated with a feast prepared by the parents of the bride. After much dancing and singing, the young couple settled into the wigwam of the girl's parents. She had two younger brothers, not yet married, who were immensely proud of having their sister married to a famous warrior. In this marriage, Ottucke owned only what he brought to the wigwam as his personal possessions. If they decided to divorce in the future, he would simply move out and take with him only his personal belongings.

Moosu was named after his habit of munching edible fern roots in the manner of the moose. Every Indian boy was encouraged to have a very close friend, and so it was with Ottucke and Moosu. As young braves, they hunted a great deal together often going on long excursions in their canoe lasting for days. In the way of young animals, Ottucke was the leader and Moosu was content to follow.

This day they had traveled two days north on the Saco river hunting for deer. Coming around a bend in the river, they saw a small buck deer, his head bent down, taking water from the stream. Due to the extreme range, Ottucke, in the front seat, silently lay down his paddle and grabbed his bow and arrow while motioning Moosu to continue paddling. Taking a kneeling position and notching his arrow, he waited silently while Moosu closed the range to the buck. The deer raised his head and exposed his body in a three quarters angle facing the canoe as Ottucke released his arrow. At this extreme range the arrow imbedded itself low in the shoulder--not a vital area. In an instant, it whirled and bounded into the woods. Now both paddled furiously to the bank of the stream.

The trail leading upward was easily followed through the heavy foliage disturbed by the passage of the buck. As the woods opened up, the signs dwindled until finally they had only blood drops to follow. After about a quarter mile, Moosu wanted to give up the chase, but Ottucke was insistent. “He is wounded; soon he will tire”, he said, admonishing Moosu as he continued to follow the steep trail. The trees continued to thin as they continued upward and it appeared to Ottucke that the deer was headed over the ridge ahead to the protection of the thick cover on the opposite side.

When they topped the ridge, they saw him a short distant ahead, limping and weak from loss of blood. As they approached, it became possible to dispatch him with one arrow placed so as to not mar the best part of the hide.

As Ottucke and Moosu began to gut the dead animal, Moosu spoke directly to the animal in his soft Algonquin dialect: "Ottucke you were very brave to run so far. I am sorry that you must die, but my family and the family of

Ottucke, who is named after you, need your flesh to sustain us. Our women need your skin to make beautiful buckskin shirts and leggings for our family. We will use your sinew to sew our moccasins and our clothing. We will even use your hooves to make glue for our baskets. The great Gluskap has seen your valor and will create you again as a turtle or an owl. Now we must take you to our village."

Those were the words spoken instinctively to another living creature who was immortal, as were Moosu and Ottucke. The deer had been created and placed in the forest for the use of the Indians and it was proper to acknowledge its role in sustaining them.

After carrying the deer carcass back to the summit of the ridge they had just come over, they sat for a few moments at the base of a huge dead pine that had been struck by lightning. The wide vertical split in the bark of the tree marked the path of the lightning bolt in its search to discharge its tremendous energy. The ground was covered with pine needles which hid a rough scrabble of loose gravel and dirt. Ottucke, idly pushing away the pine needles with his foot, noticed a darker band of material that seemed to run in a line down the slope. Taking out his knife, he tested the substance and was surprised that it was not hard like a rock, but seemed malleable. After cutting off a small piece with his knife, he took it in his hand and said to his companion, "Moosu, feel the weight of this material. It might serve well to carry the fishing line to the deep waters of the lake. Curious, they cut off several pieces and thrust them inside the carcass of the deer which they now proceeded to carry down to their canoe.

Back at the village, they began to dissect the deer carcass in front of Moosu's wigwam. Coming upon the pieces of the strange heavy material, they tried to shape it into fishing lines sinkers with their knives. Ottucke threw a small piece into a nearby fire where it landed on the flat surface of a rock. After a few seconds, the clump of material seemed to diminish, and as Ottucke watched, a thin stream of material ran down the super heated surface of the rock into the fire. The surface of the flow had a metallic sheen. Excited, they got a heavy black metal trade pot and began to heat the remaining material over the fire. After awhile it melted, and they found they could skim off the black slag-like material on top leaving molten metal. Now they knew they had something like the metal the white man used to make his musket balls. They now poured the molten metal into a depression in a log watching it smoke as the wood charred around it. They poured water over it to harden it and then pried the piece of lead out of the log.

Ottucke, his eyes gleaming with excitement, picked up the piece of lead and motioned Moosu to follow him. When they were alone he spoke.

"Many times I have seen our warriors trade furs for English muskets, the black powder and the heavy balls that kill. We have discovered one of the secrets of the white man. We can make the balls for the musket. I have seen the French make these balls. They will give us the molds to make them. First you must swear to keep our secret. You are as a brother to me, but I swear to kill you if you reveal our secret to another."

Moosu, knowing his friend well, agreed to the pact fully aware that Ottucke would not hesitate to carry out his threat.

Ottucke and Moosu went to the Jesuit, who, though on temporary assignment to their village, offered to help. He gave them a letter written to the authorities in Canada which explained the importance of the discovery and how it might be exploited by them. The two young braves then set out on an odyssey that would occupy them for the next three months.

Their destination was Saint Francis, a mission village established for Christian Indians by the French. These converted Indians, under the control of the Jesuits, could be counted on to support any military venture of the French government. It is located on the Saint Francis river south of the Saint Lawrence River now called Odanak. The descendants of the Abenaki Indians still live there.

They traveled north on the Pequacket trail until they could head west on the Androscoggin and the Waumbek to the Connecticut River. From there they headed for the Saint Francis River where the mission was located. They traveled light with the ever present extra pair of moccasins, hunting for small game as they went.

Arriving at the mission, the two young Christian braves were well received. French civil authorities at the mission immediately recognized the importance of their discovery. They dispatched a small party to Trois Rivieres with a letter requesting the bullet molds. When they returned, they carried not only two multiple cavity bullet molds, but two fine French muskets--presents for Ottucke and Moosu.

An officer of the French militia showed them how to pour the molten lead and release the halves of the mold to free the slugs. These required a small amount of whittling with a knife to cut off the slight amount of protruding metal flash. After a pleasant two week stay, they headed south well supplied with food, powder and musket balls and, of course, the two molds.

Their arrival four weeks later in the Pigwacket camp was a big event. The usual powwow and celebration marked an important event for the tribe. The two young braves steadfastly refused to divulge the location of their find.

As Ottucke explained, "It is enough that the warriors of the Pigwacket need no longer travel down the Saco and trade with the English traders for the musket balls."

They could not foresee the events that lay ahead which would have a profound effect on the existence of their entire tribe; nor could they know that only part of the value of their find was known to them. It would be many years before the full importance of their find would reveal itself to Ottucke.

View of Upper Saco River.

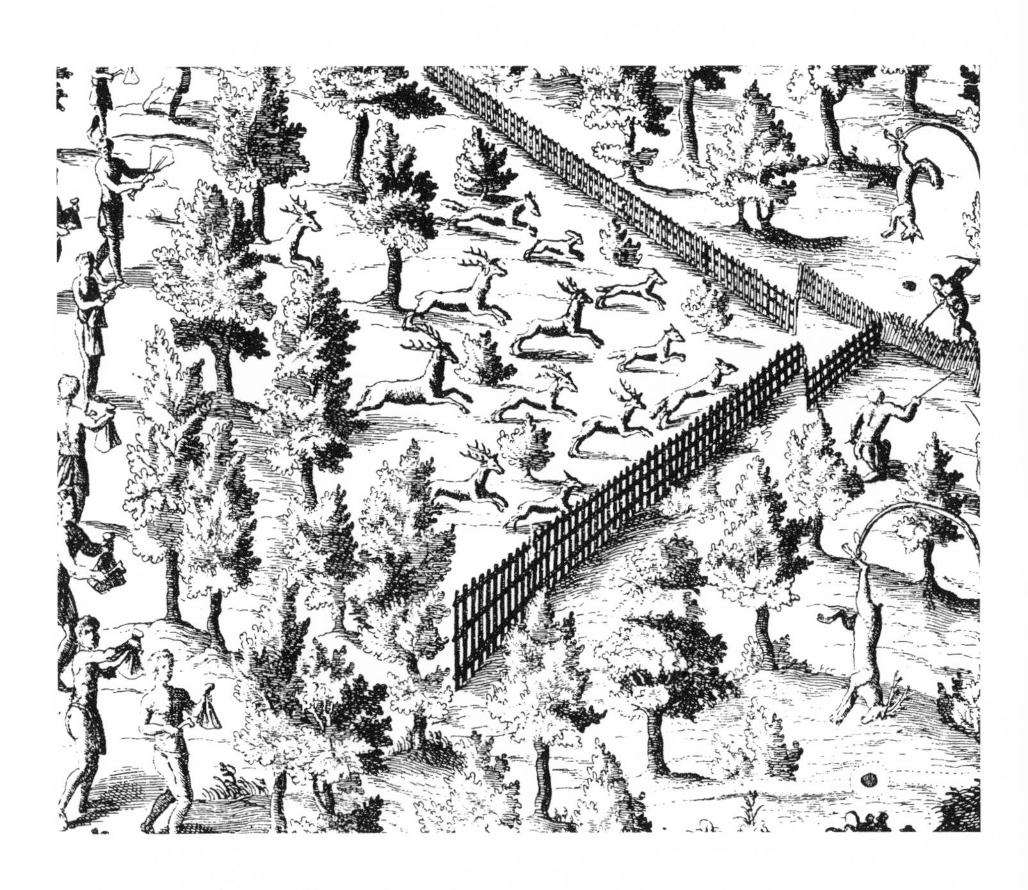

Drawing of Deer Round-up.

SUMMER AT GREAT BAY
1725

Chief Escumbuit knocked the dead ashes from his pipe and reached for his tobacco pouch for a refill. It was early afternoon in late June of 1725 and he had just refused more fresh oysters, the shells opened by the heat of the nearby fire. The squaws and children returned with baskets of raw oysters taken from the rocks at low tide and the tribe spent the past hour eating oysters and clams. The elevated mound on which they ate and discarded their oyster and clam shells was created by countless generations of Abenaki Indians before them. The great spirit Gluskap, who taught the Indians how to inhabit the earth, came from his home on an island in the Atlantic to create this special place for the Indians. He also caused the run of the salmon, smelt and shad at the falls of the Merrimac River in the spring. When winter came, he provided deer, moose, elk and bear to feed and to clothe. The Indians believed him to be blessed with unlimited powers. For example, they believed he was capable of flying from the North Pole to the South Pole in a single day.

They were well settled into their indolent summer routine of fishing, hunting for seals and porpoise, and eating. The overland party arrived at their summer camping area ahead of the canoes which also made the trip without incident. The braves went out to cut young saplings for the framework of the wigwams. A circular trench was dug about two feet deep and after the butts of the poles were buried in the ground, the tips were bent and lashed together to form a dome. Then the rolls of birch and elm bark which had been transported in the canoes were placed on the frame and overlapped in a shingle effect to provide temporary shelter for the summer. Each family cooked outside in front of their wigwam.

This was the season that freed the Indians from the sheer pressure of existing. The seashore offered more than they could eat and they did not believe in waste. With a few exceptions, most of what they ate at the seashore was perishable. The men used their canoes to fish, spear porpoise and lobster, and hunt the seal. It was the task of the women and children to harvest clams and oysters from the flats at low tide. It was the only time of the year that men and women had what we would call leisure time. One of their most important sources of food was the passenger pigeon which has been extinct since the beginning of this century. (A young boy shot the last passenger pigeon in Ohio in 1903.)

On this day, Chief Escumbuit smoked his pipe and watched with keen interest the hunt for the passenger pigeons out in the marshes. In the spring nesting season, the pigeons roosted by the millions in the oak forests of Exeter. The Indians did not interfere with them during their nesting season; but, now that the hatchlings had survived, the massive flocks had come to the seashore to forage in the tidal flats at low tide. At summer's end, they would fly south to cross the Gulf of Mexico to Central America and Mexico for their annual migration.

Chief Escumbuit watched as the braves set their snares for the pigeons. They used a coarse woven net which measured about 12 feet high and 40 feet wide. They sunk two standing poles in the mud flats about 50 feet apart, bracing them with supporting cord stays. The top line of their net had extension cords passed through holes in the tips of the poles. With the extension lines slack, the net lay unnoticed on the grass of the marsh.

As thousands of passenger pigeons foraged in the mud for edible creatures of all kinds, a line of braves crept through the marsh grass toward the unsuspecting birds. Suddenly, on cue, they stood erect and flushed the flock of birds away from them and towards the waiting net. At the signal, the brave on each side of the poles pulled in his cord raising the net and trapping dozens of the birds. Once trapped, the net was released to fall on the trapped birds which were then collected from under the net. The flocks of passenger pigeons were huge and never became wary of the Indian trap. Although this netting process was repeated time after time, the birds continued to come back to the same mud flat at low tide to feed. It can be assumed that the natives of the southern hemisphere also harvested these birds in large numbers which led to their eventual extinction. Ducks and geese had been netted in this same manner until the musket and bird-shot became commonplace, making it easier to build a crude duck blind out of marsh grass from which the Indians could bring down the birds with their muskets.

The pigeons offered a welcome relief from the summer diet of shell fish and also served as an important year round food source. The women slowly baked them on wooden frames suspended over fires to dry the meat and to extract the fat. The dried, smoked pigeons were used in stews during the winter and a typical Indian village would collect hundreds of pounds of the light fat which was used like butter.

The Chief was no longer able to take part in many of these food gathering activities. For one thing, he was already quite old in Indian terms. At 61 years, he had already lived well past the life span of the average Indian. The white man's diseases had taken their toll, but the Indian life style did not contribute to longevity. Long winters spent in smoke filled wigwams, the universal use of tobacco and the consumption of food, high in fat content, all contributed to early aging. The average Indian had a life span of about 42 years. Of course, there were exceptions, a notable one being Chief Passaconaway. This famous Chief of the Penacook Indians of Manchester and Concord, New Hampshire lived to the ripe old age of 100. He was described as being 6 foot 2 inches tall and weighing about 210 pounds.

Escumbuit did enjoy going out in his son-in-law's canoe from which they fished with drop lines. When he had been a boy, the Indians used fish hooks made out of the hollow bones of birds which were split length-wise then whittled to make a hook at one end with the other end drilled to receive the fishing line. Now, they fished with metal fish hooks provided by the English traders, who operated along the coast.

The traders were a mixed blessing for the Indians. In the beginning, they were the means through which the Indians improved their lives by trading beaver furs for metal objects. Items, which would seem to have little value to us, were prized by them. Metal pots for cooking, hatchets and axes to chop down trees, metal hoes and shovels for farming were all wondrous additions for the Stone Age Indian. Add to this metal fish hooks, woolen blankets, muskets, gun powder and musket balls and you begin to see some disruptive changes creeping into their culture.

But the traders' greatest disservice to the Indians was to introduce alcohol. There is nothing in the history of the Indians to indicate that they had ever learned the art of distilling alcohol. The Indians, raised in a culture which encouraged violence, often reverted to their savage state under the influence of alcohol. In the various attempts at lasting peace between the Colonists and the Indians was the implicit promise of the Colonists to stop the sale of rum and whiskey to the young braves. The problem was that the Colonists had no control over the renegade traders who plied the coast of Maine with their goods. Many of the crude, lawless types, who carried on trade with the Indians, were as unscrupulous as they were greedy. In the early 1700's, when the colonists were almost driven out of their border settlements by the marauding Indians and their French sponsors, the English traders continued to supply them with guns, powder and balls as well as rum. In this regard, the English had a distinct advantage over the French.

The Indians became dependent upon British goods. The quality and prices were superior to that of the French and they were much closer. Some of the Indian chiefs came to realize they were being used by the French, but counter arguments by the Jesuits in the Indian settlements carried more weight. After all, they did have a strong case to make against the colonists.

"The English is your enemy and our enemy. We have proved to you that the English are also the enemies of our Great Spirit we call God. When you make your peace treaties with the English they take it as their right to build garrisons and forts on the Saco River, the Penobscot and the Kennebec. They push their settlements up the Merrimac and soon they will drive you from the hunting grounds of your ancestors. We, who live with you as Indians, are your friends. Together we must drive the English out of your homeland."

The last thing the French wanted for the English and the Indians was to conclude a lasting peace; so, they continued to try to commit the Indians in a manner from which they could not retreat. It all came down to an exercise in European power politics; in this instance, the French were much more skilled at it.

The French commanders with whom Chief Escumbuit fought during the 1690's and early 1700's took wine with their meals, even in the field. Their culture demanded that wine be as much a part of their daily life as bread, meat and vegetables. It followed that victorious raids against the English settlements were celebrated by breaking out a keg of wine for Frenchmen and Indians alike. It was not possible to carry such luxuries on long winter forays where a man was hard pressed to carry his musket in mittened hands while carrying only the bare necessities. But, in those cases in which they were transported to their intended target by French sloops and other fighting ships, the Frenchmen were well supplied from the ship's stores.

Escumbuit adopted this happy French custom as a young brave, and developed a cultivated taste for good wine during his long visit to France in 1706 and 1707. Now, some years later, he enjoyed drinking even though he had to resort to drinking the cheap rum or whiskey obtained from the traders. Unlike many Indians, he did not get out of control when he drank. He even kept a small store of spirits in his wigwam which he used on special occasions. When he got depressed over his fall from greatness, he could recapture the good feeling of the old days by downing a cup of rum or whiskey. It was then, with little prompting, that he would begin to describe his glory days to anyone who would listen. There was never a shortage of young braves eager to hear of the days when the English fled in terror before the Abenaki warriors. Story telling was the Indian way of capturing the past and preserving it in the minds of the younger members of the tribe.

This night was such a night. A golden path to the moon was reflected directly at them from the smooth waters of the bay at high tide. They had eaten well, and after a half a cup of rum, the Chief, his mind far away, gazed at the distorted reflection of the moon while smoking his pipe.

His son-in-law knew the mood of the Chief well. At a break in the camp-fire talk, he addressed his father-in-law, respectfully saying, "The mind of our Chief is as the white clouds over the edge of the sea in the blue sky. If the clouds could speak to us now, I am sure they would have wonderful stories to tell us."

"I was thinking of my youth and my first war party against the English", he answered.

"Can you tell us of the raid so we too can share the glory of the great Abenaki victory?" prompted another young brave.

With that, knowing he had a receptive audience, Chief Escumbuit began to tell the story of his raids with the Frenchman, Hertel, against the settlers at Pemequid, Salmon Falls, and Portsmouth in 1688.

The English and French had been at peace for ten years, but actions by the English along their border with the Indians had infuriated the Abenakis. A Frenchman, named Saint Castin, had established a trading post at what is now known as Castin, Maine. He had married the daughter of Chief Madockawando and had turned Indian himself. The English had raided and destroyed his trading post and Castin escaped capture by going into the woods with the Indians. In retribution, he offered gunpowder, lead and tobacco to any Indian who would take up his musket against the English.

Near the mouth of the Saco River at Biddeford, some drunken English sailors went out in a rowboat on a lark. Sighting an Indian squaw in a canoe with a baby, one of the sailors offered the opinion that Indian babies, like young otters or beavers, are able to swim at birth. After much arguing pro and con, one of them shouted, "Let's find out!" after which they overtook the canoe and capsized it.

The squaw recovered the baby and managed to swim ashore; but, the baby died a little while later. The squaw was the daughter of an important Chief named, Moxus. News of this atrocity inflamed all of the Maine Indian tribes.

Another development setting the scene for disaster for the Colonists was their withdrawal of about 500 men from the forts and garrisons of the frontier. The news of the landing in England of the Prince of Orange had sparked a revolution against the despotic King James II with great political repercussions in Boston. A large number of men manning the coastal outposts had been recalled to Boston. This left the frontier almost defenseless. It was under these conditions that the Indians fell with fury upon the almost helpless settlements in the spring.

Father Thury of the Penobscot mission pressed for volunteers. When word reached the Pigwacket village in Fryeburg, Ottucke and his friend Moosu were the first braves to step forward. They joined Father Thury's Indians from the Penobscot, and others who came down from the Kennebec. They were part of the war party which fell upon Fort Charles at Pemequid near the tip of the peninsula jutting into the Atlantic Ocean south of Damariscotta, Maine. This wooden stockade fort, protected by eight cannons, was built to replace a lesser redoubt destroyed in 1676. Its 30 defenders under Lieutenant James Weems were all that remained from the original garrison of 156 men, the bulk of the fort's complement having been withdrawn as a result of the political upheaval in Boston.

The attacking force had over 200 Indians, all Christian converts. According to Father Thury's written account, "The Indians made their vows to the Virgin immediately before the attack while their squaws back at the villages told unceasing beads and offered countless prayers for victory."

The Indians' surprise attack gave them possession of several houses behind the fort which was occupied mostly by women and children, the men being away at work. They were able to keep up a heavy fire on the fort from the houses and from behind a large outcropping of rock which rose prominently between the fort and the bay. Skillfully using this cover, the Indians managed to pick off 16 of Weems' men with their musket fire. The next day, Weems surrendered on a promise of life and liberty to himself and all his followers. Nevertheless, when he emerged from the fort with the 14 surviving soldiers and some women and children who had fled there for safety, the Indians fell upon them, slaughtering without pity. Chief Madockawando, who had a reputation for moderation, insisted that Captain Weems and five of his soldiers be spared. The attack took a heavy toll on the residents of the surrounding settlements. Many were killed or taken captive in the houses and fields surrounding the fort. A French historian claims the total casualties of the attack were 80 men, women and children killed. Given a full complement of defenders, on their guard against an attack, there is little doubt that the fort and inhabitants of the settlement could have repelled the Indians.

Parkman, the Harvard historian, says that, "except for the slain, the behavior of the victors is said to be credible. They tortured no-one and their chiefs broke the casks of wine in the fort in order to keep their warriors under control. Father Thury, who was present, writes that he exhorted the Indians to refrain from drunkenness and cruelty. He adds that, as a consequence, they did not take a single scalp.

Ottucke's lethal war club had taken its terrible toll before and after the surrender of the fort. When this attack was complete he had cut five new notches on his war-club. Moosu had also fought well and had two notches to his credit. The war-party burned the fort and the surrounding houses and the surviving prisoners were taken to Thury's mission village on the Penobscot. From there, they were taken to Canada to an uncertain fate.

The war now ran like wildfire through the settlements of Maine and New Hampshire. Sixteen fortified houses fell into the hands of the enemy and the entire coastal area was desolated by marauding bands of Indians.

That summer, Ottucke and Moosu added many notches to their war clubs. As winter approached, Massachusetts sent out a large force of untrained militia to try to engage the enemy. But after driving off a large band of Indians near Portland, things seemed to quiet down and the troops were withdrawn once again to Boston. The settlers became complacent about the threat of danger from the Indians.

Unknown to the English, Count Frontenac, the governor of Canada, organized three separate war parties in Canada, their dual purpose to try to obtain some cheap victories to buoy the spirits of the Canadian people, who were at a low ebb from their incessant wars with the Iroquois Indians. The second motive was to put the English on notice that the French, though in a weakened state, still had a sting.

One of these parties was sent to attack Schenectady, New York, and the remaining two were assigned separate targets in Maine and New Hampshire.

On January 28, 1689, Francois Hertel left Trois Rivieres with 24 Frenchmen and 25 Abenakis from the missionary refuge which had been established for them by the French authorities. After an incredible three months march through winter storms, they lay hidden on the outskirts of Salmon Falls, NH, which lies up the Saco River not far from Biddeford. Among the volunteers from the Pickgwacket tribe in Fryeburg were Ottucke and Moosu. Scouts reconnoitering the settlement found a fortified house and two stockade forts intended as a refuge for the settlers in case of alarm.

Hertel divided his force into three parties which attacked simultaneously. The settlers, unconscious of danger, were in their beds. No watch had been set even at the so called forts. When the Indians burst in, the action was short and brutal. About 30 persons of all ages and sexes were tomahawked or knocked in the head with war-clubs, and 54 people, mostly women and children, were made prisoner. They put to ashes the various houses and barns of the settlement and killed the cattle. Scouts reported that English re-enforcements were enroute from the Portsmouth area so they rounded up their prisoners and began their retreat.

A pursuing force of 150 Englishmen caught up with them about sunset after they had crossed the Wooster River via a small bridge. Here, they made a stand and a fire fight took place across the river. There were killed and wounded on both sides. Hertel's son was badly wounded and Moosu, Ottucke's friend, was killed by a musket ball to the head. Hertel's force made its escape in the night. He turned one of the male prisoners over to the Indians, who in turn tortured and killed him. The Indians also cruelly tormented the children and infants in the party. Then the party headed for one of the Indian villages located on the Kennebec river.

When they arrived, they learned that the third French war party had already arrived and gone and were headed for Casco Bay. This party, under the command of an officer named Portneuf and his lieutenant Courtemanche, consisted of 50 French and 60 Abenakis from the St. Francis mission, who had been joined by a large force of local Abenaki Indians. They had taken a leisurely trip south from Canada, hunting and fishing along the way and now, they were headed for their objective--Fort Loyal in Portland.

Hertel immediately reversed his route and headed to join the other force, leaving his wounded son with the

Indians. Ottucke, burning to revenge the death of his friend Moosu, was sent ahead with another scout to catch the Portneuf party to delay them until Hertel could catch up. Saint Castin, who was there with his band from the Penobscot, swelled the combined forces to between 400 and 500 men.

Fort Loyal, a palisade fort of eight cannons, stood on a rise at the foot of what is now known as India Street in Portland, Maine. Sylvanus Davis, a local trader, was in command. Close by were four blockhouses and a small village which the fort had been built to protect. They could muster about 80 men to protect the fort and the block houses. The fields had been cleared for about a half a mile around the settlement.

As the French force approached, two of their forward scouts captured a straggler in the fields; and their cries, as they scalped their victim, alerted the fort. Davis wanted to confine his men to the fort to repel the enemy, but an eager young Lieutenant Thaddeus Clark, on his own initiative, set out with 30 young volunteers to find and engage the enemy. When they came to the edge of the open field, they noticed some cows staring over the fence at something in the woods. Correctly guessing, he had found the enemy. He led his men in a charge where, at close quarters, they received a volley so concentrated as to send them running back to the protection of the fort. Only four men, all wounded, made it back to the fort.

By nightfall, all of the occupants of the block house had withdrawn to the fort where the entire force was assembled together with their frightened families. The next day, Portneuf and his men burned the entire village.

Then, with the use of shovels and equipment taken from the village, they dug trenches within 50 yards of the fort. From the protection of the trenches, his men were able to burrow ever nearer the walls of the fort without losing a single man. At this point they called upon the English to surrender. Davis' request for a six day delay was refused, and, the following morning, the fighting broke out anew. After four days, they got close enough to place some fire wood and quantities of tar against the palisade. The defenders, having expended most of their ammunition, vainly trying to dislodge the Indians, finally asked for a parley.

The French were dressed and painted like the Indians so it was only at this point that Davis realized there were Frenchmen in the group. Davis then shouted to the assailants asking whether there were any Frenchmen among them, asking further if they would give them quarter. After the French acknowledged they were in command, Davis asked if they would give quarter to his men, women and children. He demanded they be given the liberty to march to the next English town and to be provided with a French escort to protect them from the Indians. Davis' final demand to the French Commander was that if he accepted his terms, he should hold up his hand and swear by the great and living God that these conditions would be performed; all of which did he solemnly swear.

The men, women and children then filed through the gate and laid down their arms whereupon they were abandoned to the Indians by the French commander. The Indians immediately set upon them murdering many and carrying off the remainder as prisoners. For some unknown reason, Davis was spared and taken to Canada together with three of his men. There he met Count Frontenac, the governor of Canada, who became very angry when notified of the betrayal by his commander Portneuf. Nevertheless, the triumphant success of the three war parties had accomplished everything that Frontenac had hoped for. The Governor wrote: "You cannot believe the joy that these slight successes has caused and how much it contributes to raise the people (Canadians) from their dejection and terror." (Again we see how terror inflicted on innocent victims provided comfort to others.)

The young warrior, Ottucke, only 24 years old, had wielded his war club with abandon at Salmon Falls, and had fought bravely in the action at the Wooster River. His savagery against the Salmon Falls prisoners after the death of Moosu and here at Fort Loyal marked him for attention, not only by the Abenakis, but their French allies as well.

At his camp-fire, on the shore of Great Bay, Chief Escumbuit had been describing this campaign to his rapt audience in his direct manner. He did not dwell on the political goals of the English and the French--the Indian mind did not recognize such complex emotions as conscience and guilt. To him, things were very clear. The English were his enemy because they were stealing the land of his ancestors and they must be driven out of his land. The French were his friends because they were the enemies of the English. Now, he signaled the end of his story by knocking the cold ashes from his pipe and drinking the last inch of rum from his cup.

There was a moment of silence, and then a youngster asked, "Was it then that the Chief's Council that made you the War Chief of the Pigwackets?"

Escumbuit answered, "Yes, when we returned to our village, I was elected War Chief by the Chief's Council; but my heart was heavy for the loss of my friend Moosu."

The next, day two young braves came back from their lobster hunt with news for the Chief. An English trader, by the name of Newsholm, had hailed them and asked them if they could take him to Chief Escumbuit. He had sailed up the river looking for potential customers for his trade goods. He knew many small bands of Indians spent their summer on the shore of the bay and had traded with them in previous years. He also knew that he would find Escumbuit there.

The Indians from Escumbuit's band brought furs they had trapped over the winter in anticipation of this event. It was a festive occasion for the squaws, who prepared mental shopping lists well in advance. Newsholm operated on the fringe of this hostile territory between the Indians and the English with complete immunity. Access to quality trade goods at cheap prices was vital to the Indians and they needed a reliable outlet for the furs they had to sell. It was a practical relationship which both sides accepted as necessary to their existence.

The messengers said that Captain Newsholm wanted to powwow with the Chief before the trading began. Normally, the trading was done out in the bay. The Indians would come out by canoe with their squaws and the trading would take place over the rail of the 40-foot sailboat. That way Captain John Newsholm could maintain control of the Indians without having to worry about theft or having them rummage through his wares unsupervised.

Escumbuit sent a message via the two braves that he would arrive at the sailboat the following day about midmorning. After he and the captain finished their powwow, the village could complete the trade with the captain. The

Chief already had some idea what the parley would be about and wanted some time to gather his thoughts.

The next morning, the Chief was welcomed aboard like a valued friend. The Captain was a friendly man with a hearty personality which wore well with the Indians. He had treated Chief Escumbuit's followers well in previous years and they trusted him. He handed him a bag of tobacco and motioned him to a chair on the deck of the boat where they both fell silent for a moment as they filled their pipes and lit up. The Chief handed the bag of tobacco back to the Captain, but he waved it off indicating it was a present. He then had one of his Indian crew go below to draw two tumblers of rum for him and his guest. The rum was kept under lock and key in the Captain's cabin so as to not tempt his crewmen. The Captain then hung the only existing key back around his neck by its cord.

John Newsholm had traveled the coast trading with the Indians for years. He had an Indian crew, and over the years, he learned how to speak Algonquin. He began carefully taking care that the Chief was able to follow his line of thought, saying,

"Chief, it is ten years since I first talked to you about your silver mine. It is still a mystery to the English that some of the musket balls fired by the Abenakis have a high silver content mixed with the lead.[7] I learned from

---

[7] Colby's Indian History (Chapter21) **Silver bullets**: During the long and bloody struggle between the English and the Indians that drifted back and forth between Maine and New Hampshire and the French rendezvous in Canada, the Indians sometimes used bullets which contained more than half silver. These remarkable missiles became the

the Pigwacket tribe that these musket balls did not come from the French or from the English traders on the coast. They told me that it was you who made the musket balls for the tribe until you left to live with your new tribe. They say that only you know the location of the mine.

---

wonder of the whites and the source from whence they were obtained was a mystery. To this day the secret has not been learned, but how near it once came to being known is told by an old resident of Berlin, New Hampshire.

Some years before Berlin was settled, Mr. Benjamin Russell came through the woods from Newry, Maine on a hunting excursion as far as what is now called Old Goose Eye Mountain, but not meeting the success anticipated, he started from that mountain to go back through to Newry, but got lost. It was four or five days before he, at last, found where he was, but when he did he came out on Bear River, nearly famished with hunger. When wandering around, about to descend a very steep place on the side of the mountain, and finding his hatchet a hindrance, he threw it ahead of him down the declivity. To his surprise the tool embedded its edge in what looked to him a solid rock. Upon reaching the place he found it was stuck in a vein of lead, so soft that it could easily be chipped. He stopped to cut out three or four pounds of the ore, and, putting it in his pack resumed his journey, thinking it would be an easy matter to find the isolated spot again. He did succeed in finding his way out of the wilderness, and soon after, he sent some of the ore to Boston to be assayed. It was found to contain more than sixty percent of silver. It was now evident where the Indians had found the ore for the "silver bullets." Elated over his accidental discovery, Mr. Russell started to find the place again, but after days of anxious search, he failed to find any sign which revealed the rich vein of ore. This search he repeated from time to time, but he was never able to find the place, and to this day it remains undiscovered. Without a shadow of doubt somewhere between Old Goose Eye Mountain and Newry lies a vein of ore which would be a fortune to him who should find it.

Bailey K. Davis (1905)

They say you killed one of their braves and wounded another for trying to steal your secret.

"My good friend, the secret does you no good. I know you cannot return to the territory of the Pigwacket because the families of the two you killed and wounded have sworn to kill you. But, I'm your friend; I can be trusted. You know I have never cheated in my price for your furs. If you can tell me how to find the mine, I can arrange to bring the lead and the silver to Boston where I can sell it for much money. I have friends among the Pigwackets, who will help me do this. If you will tell me how to find the mine, I will give you five parts of each ten parts of the value of the metal. I can bring the papers written by the lawyers of the English which will guarantee my words."

Chief Escumbuit was direct in his answer to Newsholm.

"As I have told you in the past, I have no reason to not trust you. You have always been honest with me and my people. It has not always been so with other English traders. But I do not trust the paper of the white man. The Indians have placed their totem on many treaties of the white man and the leaders of the white man have signed in their own manner; yet, the white man has not kept the spirit of the treaties. They do not keep their word. They continue to build their forts against the spirit of the treaties. Then my people must go on the war path to drive them back to their own land. If I show you the place of the shining metal, I must be with you. But I cannot go to this place because I have many enemies there. If the spirits decide to change these things, I will go with you."

Sensing that the Chief was immovable on this subject, the Captain decided to tack in another direction.

"I understand why you do not want to share your secret with me. I do not take it as a personal insult, but I understand the things which worry you. I have a new idea for you to think about. As you know, the English have allowed their people to open trading posts on the frontier. Only the white men on the council in Boston can give a permit to open trading posts, but I know many of these men. I have long sailed the waters of the coast trading with the Indians, but now I grow old and I wish to settle down in one place. I would like to build a trading post on the Salmon Falls River at Rollingsford, close to Dover. There are two Indian villages in the area, the Quamphegan and the Cocheco. This is a good location for a trading post. I wish to trade in peace with the Indians as I do now from my boat. For that I need you as my partner. It will be you, who will tell the Indians that I deal fair with the Indians. They know you and trust you to speak the truth. For this I will build you a cabin on the river and give you one part in ten of the money I make from my trades with the Indians. On this, you can live in comfort like the white man.

"From here, I sail to Boston to load new trading goods. If you agree to my offer, I will apply for the permit. If the council gives me approval, I will need your totem on the agreement. I will return to Great Bay in two months to give you the news."

Chief Escumbuit, though unschooled in white man's dealings, recognized this was an offer he could not refuse. In his mind, it would not be an agreement until it bore his totem; so he readily agreed to wait for the results of Captain Newsholm's visit to Boston. The Captain's offer to use Chief Escumbuit as his front man for the Indians was made with the design to earn the Chief's trust; the silver mine was still at the back of his thinking.

Finally, the Captain said, "Let's have one more drink. Then you can call your tribe to the boat."

As the trading proceeded briskly with the Indians, Chief Escumbuit stayed on deck as the guest of the Captain, but his mind was still on the Captain's proposal. He could not think of any way to profit from the silver without risking loss of control. He thought of his experiences in France and the effect the money from the silver would have on his family. His final thought, however, could not leave him.

"Better that I die with the secret than have it stolen from me. Maybe something will come of this trading post plan."

The powwow with the Captain awakened unrest in the Chief that had been long suppressed. He was torn between his Indian roots and the life and culture he had enjoyed during his long visit to France. The passage of time had not dimmed his memory of the acclaim he had enjoyed in Paris. His awareness of the potential for wealth the silver mine offered was the goad that prevented him from rejecting dreams of a return to his former greatness.

Picture of Pemequid Rock.

PIGWACKETS ELECT NEW WAR CHIEF 1689-1697

To follow the course of Escumbuit's military adventures, we must resume our narrative from the end of his campfire account of his adventures with Hertel at Salmon Falls, and Portneuf at Port Loyal in Portland, Maine in 1689. After these victories, there was a lull in the fighting, and many of the Indians, including young Ottucke, returned to their villages. Now, a fighting legend at the age of 24, he was obliged to take a break from his raids against the settlers.

Massachusetts launched some counter attacks and sent a fleet to Quebec in an attempt to capture it for the English. The invasion failed, but some of the Indians were having second thoughts about continuing the war against the colonies. They were torn between their desire to trade for the cheap British goods and the pressure from their French allies to carry the war to the English settlers.

The Jesuits at their missions in the Abenaki villages were also under pressure. Their primary concern was the conversion of the Indians, but their financial support depended on the good graces of the Canadian Civil authorities. They knew that in order to enjoy the continuing financial support of the authorities, they had to also serve the political aims of these same people.

The four areas for which Frontenac was responsible were the far west, the Hudson River Valley, Newfoundland and Arcadia. The French believed they owned all the lands in Maine down to the Kennebec River while the British believed their territory extended up to the Saint Croix River in Canada. This disputed area in Maine was known as Arcadia. Hence, the origin of *The Arcadia National Park*. Soon the war in Arcadia would heat up again, and Ottucke, known as the ruthless Chief Escumbuit, would play a major role.

Ottucke returned to his Pigwacket village in Fryeburg after the capture of Fort Loyal in Portland. The prisoners were taken to one of the villages on the Kennebec, but Ottucke was not needed to take them on to Canada. The Frenchmen, who had been on the raid, were insistent, saying that he should stay in the area and continue to harass the settlers. The other Pigwacket warriors returning with him had spread the word of his exploits and the chiefs of the village realized that they were going to have to give him some sort of recognition.

After the customary celebration which followed a successful war party, the chiefs council had a powwow to discuss elevating Ottucke to a War Chief. Unlike most military organizations where a person can be promoted through a variety of ranks from private to general, the Indians elected only Civil and War chiefs. The election process was based on merit. As it was also common for sons of great chiefs to be elected chiefs in turn, it would be incorrect to suggest that politics did not enter into the selection process.

After the usual smoking of the sacramental pipe, each chief of the large village had his chance to deliver his solemn comments on Ottucke's merit. They recounted his exploits on the Iroquois raid in his younger years and now the large number of notches he had cut into his war club after the raids on the settlements. There was no dissent as to whether he was worthy. It came down to the formality of choosing a suitable name for him. He would carry this assigned name for the rest of his life.

After a series of names were suggested and rejected, the oldest, most respected chief on the council, signaled to be heard.

"Great chiefs of the Pigwacket council. Hear me speak. I have been a chief on your council even before the pale face came. When all our hunting was with the bow and arrow and the women scraped the hide of the deer with flint and the bone from the moose. Many things have changed, but there can be no change in the one we would make our War Chief. Never has the danger to our tribe been so great. In my youth the white man sent his demons who made our people sick, and we few who lived could not bury the dead--so many were they. Now the white man comes with his stone forts and his cannons, and his warriors multiply as mushrooms in the forest. Against these mighty forces, Gluskap, our Great Spirit, has sent us a warrior who, like Gluskap himself, is invincible. The white man cannot kill him. The notches on his war club tell us that. For all these things I say his name must be *Assacumbuit*."

Like all Indian words, the name created a picture in the minds of the assembled chiefs. It pictured a superlative that only an Indian would recognize, but it struck a strong chord of acceptance with the other chiefs. With little more discussion it was agreed that their newest, youngest War Chief would be named *Chief Assacumbuit,* and be known as *Nescambiouit*[8] by the French, and as *Escumbuit* or *Old Escambuit* by the English.

In the 1690's, Arcadia was a lawless area which attracted renegades of all races and nationalities. There were both French and English privateers who engaged in a form of piracy on the high seas, preying on each other and on the settlements of the area. Pirates of many different nationalities from the West Indies preyed on all of the above. Added to that were renegade Indians looking for scalps and booty.

After the earlier *no quarter* attacks of the French and Indians in which most of the victims were slaughtered in a reign of terror, the French began to pay for live prisoners and scalps. After that, many prisoners were spared and taken to Canada in order to collect the payment that awaited them.

---

[8] Abbe N. F. Maurault, Histoire des Abenakis (p.330) Jesuit missionary at the Indian mission set up for refugees in Saint Francis, spells his name as Naskanbiwit and gives its Indian meaning as "He who is so important and raised so high by his merit, that thought cannot reach his greatness."

"Indian Place Names of New England" by John C Huden lists Escumbuit Island, Rockingham County, New Hampshire as a Micmac name meaning "At the watching place." The Micmac Indians were from the most northern part of Maine and we know that Escumbuit was a Pigwacket Indian from Fryeburg, Maine near Conway. If we accept Huden's meaning of Escumbuit Island, the most likely meaning of the name for an individual would be, "He who watches," or simply, "The look-out." On the basis of credentials alone, Abbe Maurault, who lived with the Abenaki Indians and was their historian, appears more authoritative.

During this era there were five men to every woman in Canada so, in general, women and young females were encouraged in every way to resign themselves to their fate by converting to Catholicism and marrying into Canadian society. Also a certain number of both sexes were adopted into Indian families. When given a chance to be returned to their own families, many of the captives chose to remain with their Canadian and Indian families.

After Escumbuit and the French had destroyed Pemequid in 1689, and following their ravage of Fort Loyal and Salmon Falls, only Wells, York and Kittery continued active. In July of 1693, Chief Madockawando together with 12 other chiefs signed a peace treaty with the English. As it went against French interests, Father Thury cleverly used Chief Taxous' jealousy of Chief Madockawando to induce him and his Indians to attack Wells and York in order to negate the treaty.

Villebon, brother-in-law of Portneuf, was sent to govern Arcadia, where he arrived with many gifts for the Indians. In a special ceremony, Chief Taxous was made his brother. Villieu was put in charge of the Indians, who were given large quantities of small arms, powder and lead. They marched on snow shoes all the way to Durham, New Hampshire, where they killed 104 men, women and children, and took 27 prisoners. This raid broke the treaty with the English.

It should be emphasized that not all of the Jesuits were as militant as Father Thury. Many dedicated themselves to the conversion of the Indians, refusing to become embroiled in the war. Indeed, some of them were accused by their fellow Jesuits and French authorities of favoring the English. The names of the activists appear regularly in historical accounts of the conflict. Thury and Simon were prominent as was Father Sebastian Rale. The Bigot brothers, both Jesuits, were involved in inciting the Indians as well. (Later you will read an account of Protestant Chaplain Frye of Andover, killing and scalping Indians with Lovewell.)

In 1696, Captains March,[9] Wing and Bancroft took a large work force to Pemequid to build a stone fort to replace Fort Charles which was destroyed by the Indians in 1689 with the attendant tragic loss of 80 men, women and children. This was the Colonists' northernmost defense against the French in Arcadia. Having failed to occupy and hold the fort after Weems' surrender in 1689, a strong English presence sat like a bone in the throat of the French. Its level of importance to the Colonists is indicated by their decision to spend 20,000 pounds (one third of their entire budget for 1692), for its construction. When completed in 1693, Governor Phipps of the Massachusetts Colony wrote to a colleague: "The fort is strong enough to resist all the Indians in America." The events that followed the fort's completion made a mockery of this proud boast.

Fort William Henry was impressive indeed! It was enclosed by walls six feet thick, ranging 10 to 20 feet in height. These walls enclosed a square measuring roughly 108 feet to a side. The 28 gun ports in the outer wall intimidated prospective attackers with 18 cannons. Facing the entrance to the harbor, to the west, a large round tower 28 feet high was built into a corner of the quadran-

---

[9] Author's note: Prior to his service at Pemequid, John March had a boat building business on the Merrimac River in Andover. A later account in this story describes how he survived a surprise tomahawk attack by Escumbuit and two other Indian chiefs in Portland, Maine.

gle. The base of this tower was built around the large rock outcropping which shielded the Indians so effectively in their 1689 raid. The opposite corner had a fan shaped tower and the remaining two corners had inner towers. The large inner quadrangle held separate officers and troops quarters that were well appointed with fireplaces and other comforts. Late in the summer, before construction was finished, D'Iberville sailed into the harbor with three French ships and a complement of Indians aboard. Apparently, the fort appeared too formidable to risk an attack, and he put about and returned to his home port at Placentia in Newfoundland. With the satisfaction that comes from having invested their money wisely, officials in Boston felt certain that their Arcadia outpost was invincible.

But all was not well at Fort William Henry. The quality of the mortar was poor, having been mixed with beach sand and clay with little lime in the mix. When they test-fired two of their cannons, the walls on which they were mounted cracked. The designers' strategy of enclosing the rock outcropping inside the base of their huge round tower to deny its cover to future attackers was resourceful, but in leaving the garrison's only well outside the northwest wall, they were like a warrior baring his Achilles' tendon to the slash of his adversary's knife. Troops can go hungry for long periods, but they can't survive long without water.

The famous Pierre Le Moyne D'Iberville arrived early in August of 1696 in command of a squadron of three French sloops among which were the *Envieus* and the *Profond*. At St. Johns, Newfoundland, they met and engaged two British frigates and an auxiliary tender. They took one frigate after blowing off its mast, but the other frigate and the tender escaped in the fog. At Castin's trading post, they joined Fathers Simon and Thury and the Indians. After the usual feasting at a powpow hosted by the French, 500 Indians paddled south towards Pemequid. The following day, D'Iberville, with 100 French soldiers aboard, set sail to join the attack on Fort William Henry.

Chief Escumbuit and his Pigwacket warriors, together with the rest of the Indians, landed about ½ mile from the fort at New Harbor. The French commanders were Baron St. Castin, Captain Villieu and Montigny. From this point, Montigny is described as performing wonders by the French historians and has Escumbuit at his side. The Jesuit, Charlevoix, writes of "Montigny and his faithful Nescambiouit'. In several passages, he praises the bravery of the French officers, and bestows singular praise to Nescambiouit.

The fort was commanded by Pasco Chubb[10] from Andover, Massachusetts, together with 95 men. They had

---

[10] Andover: Symbol of New England, Claude M Fuess, (p 75): "The Strange Case Of Pasco Chubb." This man, with a name which Dickens would have been delighted to immortalize, made his entrance on the colonial scene in unobtrusive fashion but ended as the central figure in a grim and sinister episode. Thomas Chubb arrived from England in 1663, bound to Samuel Maverick for his passage money. We have the record of the marriage, May 29,1689, of Pasco Chubb, son of Thomas and Avis Chubb, to Hannah Faulkner, daughter of Edmund Faulkner, one of the original proprietors of Andover. When and how he came to Andover is unknown; but he was listed in a ":Rate made for the minister in the year 1692 for the North End of the Town Of Andover." The Chubb family had evidently come up in the world! Chubb must have accumulated some military experience, for in February, 1696, he was placed in command of the newly constructed Fort William Henry at Pemaquid, on the coast of Maine.

18 cannons and were well supplied with powder, ball and provisions.

We must return here to an earlier episode involving Chubb and a group of important Indian chiefs, who had come to the fort under a white flag. When the Indians broke the treaty by attacking the settlement at Durham, Governor Stoughton of Massachusetts wrote the priests Bigot and Thury criticizing them for breaking the peace and demanding they bring their prisoners to the fort at Pemequid. Bigot returned a defiant letter of refusal, but Father Thury, anxious to obtain the release of Indian and French prisoners held in Boston, sent a party of Indians to parley with Chubb over a possible prisoner exchange.

Chief Escumbuit was part of the group sent to parley with Chubb. Egeremet, Chief of the Machias Indians, Abenquid, and Taxous of the Norridgewacks, together with several other chiefs, made up the party of about 12 Indians. Chubb, together with 11 soldiers from the fort, met with the Indian leaders at a site outside the fort under a flag of truce.

Chubb planned his treacherous course of action well. He plied the Indians with liquor to the point of intoxication whereupon, at his signal, they attempted to capture all of the Indians. In the fight that followed, Egeremet and Abenquid and two of their Indians were murdered on the spot. The English managed to take some prisoners, but Assacumbuit and Taxous escaped.

The French rejoiced upon hearing about Chubb's betrayal of the Indians knowing that the treachery of the English played directly into the intrigues of the French. Chubb, by his ill-advised action, accomplished exactly what the French authorities had hoped for: he disturbed a hornet's nest, and news of the English betrayal swept aside all thoughts of further peace with the English. It was again time for Abenaki retribution.

After the attack on Salmon Falls and Fort Loyal in 1698, Chief Escumbuit did not remain idle. During this period, the frontier was never completely safe for the settlers. Although the French and the English were officially at peace, he continued to harass the frontier with his small war parties. News of a change of policy in France might take months to reach the Indians in the interior of Maine. Settlers were forced to live like prisoners in their garrisoned homes. No one dared to go into the woods for fishing or hunting. Small bands of Indians always lurked, looking for a chance to kill and scalp a single farmer working his property or to carry off an unwary youth.

When Chief Escumbuit had his audience with King Louis XIV, he boasted of having killed 150 of the king's enemies. Numbers have a way of failing to impress unless one thinks in terms of 150 individuals walking, talking men women and children being shot, stabbed or having their skulls crushed with war-clubs. It is simply that it took some time for the notoriety of Chief Escumbuit to capture the attention of the French and later the English. That is why his name begins to appear with some frequency in 1696. This does not mean, however, that he had not already carved many notches on his famous war club in the years leading up to 1696.

We return to Pasco Chubb and the siege of Pemequid. Although the fort was rebuilt at great expense with stone and mortar, it could not withstand cannon fire. Also, many of the soldiers were permitted to bring along their wives and children.

The 500 Indians, who landed their canoes at New Harbor, surrounded the fort, but they were unable to get close enough to make effective use of their muskets. The bastion of the rebuilt fort now enclosed the large stone outcropping from where they had directed their fire in 1689. Nevertheless, they called upon Chubb to surrender.

He responded by saying, "We will continue to fight though the ocean may be covered with French ships and the land by Indians."

That night, with great difficulty, the French unloaded two cannons plus two mortars from one of their sloops and moved them into position to fire on the fort. The two priests, Simon and Thury, labored alongside the Indians to get the guns into position. At three o'clock the next day, they opened fire on the fort with devastating results. Shortly before the shelling began, Saint Castin sent Chubb a note telling him the cannons were in position to begin shelling the fort and warned him that if he did not surrender the occupants would be given no quarter and would be turned over to the Indians. After five or six shots, Chubb ran up a white flag and asked for a parley. He offered to surrender the fort if he and all his people were protected from the Indians and sent to Boston in exchange for French and Indian prisoners held there. D'Iberville, having accepted these terms, kept his word and the men and their families were taken to a small island in the bay where they were held under the protection of the ships guns.

Upon entering the fort, they found an Indian held in chains. He had been taken during Chubb's treacherous attack during the fake prisoner exchange. He was in such deplorable condition that Escumbuit and his warriors flew into a rage and wanted to take immediate revenge on the English. With some difficulty, D'Iberville dissuaded them from this, and when the French discovered a letter written by Chubb's superiors in Boston giving him instructions to hang this prisoner, they withheld this information from Escumbuit fearing they might lose control over him and his Indians.

When Chubb returned to Boston, he was arrested and tried for cowardice and spent a few months in prison. The authorities failed to recognize that, had he resisted, the French cannon would have destroyed the fort and the Indians would have butchered the inmates. They were shocked by the seeming easy conquest of a fort which had cost them so much money to build. There is a letter in the Massachusetts archives written by Chubb asking to be pardoned.[11]

---

[11] Historical Sketches Of Andover, by Sarah Loring Bailey, (p 181), "-The Petition of Pasco Chubb late Commander of his Majestys ffort William Henry at Pemaquid, Humbly sheweth. "That yr Petitioner stands committed a Prisoner in Boston Goale for his late surrendering & delivering up the aforesd Fort and Stores thereto belonging unto his Majestys enemies.

"And whereas yr Petitioner is a very poore man, having a wife and children to Looke after wch by reason of his confinement & poverty are reduced to a meane and necessitous condition having not wherewithall either to defray his present necessary charges or to relieve his Indigent family....

"Your Petitioner therefore humbly prays that this high and hon Court will please to consider the premises so as that he may now either be Brought to his Tryall or else upon giving sufficient Bayle be delivered from his present confinement, whereby he may be enabled to take some care of his poore family for their subsistence in the hard & deare winter season."

Evidently, friends pled his case with the Boston authorities and, after his release, he went back to live with his wife in North Andover, Massachusetts. But Escumbuit had not forgotten Chubb's treachery, and the almost bloodless surrender of Pemequid had thwarted his plans to settle accounts with him. His Indian code still called for revenge. Chubb's dark destiny followed him into retirement and the Town of Andover, as well as Chubb and his wife, would be forced to pay a stiff price for his misdeeds.[12]

D'Iberville now planned to take his forces north to attack the English in their Newfoundland settlements, but he had to dispose of his prisoners. They spent August 17 and 18 destroying the fort and loading the cannon on the ships. He sent some of the prisoners to Boston with the message that the rest would be released when the English released all French and Indian prisoners. He then set sail for Penobscot Bay where he waited for some time without receiving an answer from the Governor in Massachusetts. Having run low on provisions, he sent the rest of the

---

[12] Historical Sketches of Andover, Sarah Loring Bailey, (p.122) Pasco Chubb had an unenviable reputation in his day. He was, as is related in the chapter on the Indian wars, cashiered for treasonable or inefficient conduct at Fort Pemaquid, imprisoned in Boston jail, and finally set at liberty and allowed to live in seclusion at Andover. He had married in this town a daughter of Mr. Edmond Faulkner, and previous to his military misdemeanors had been presented before the court of the county for offences. He seems to have been an unprincipled man, whose connection with Andover families brought chiefly disgrace and sorrow. He and his wife were murdered by the Indian in 1698. With their death the name perished from Andover annals.

prisoners to Boston holding only the officers. These, including Pasco Chubb, were placed in Captain Villieu's care and were later returned to Boston.

D'Iberville finally sailed north with his Canadian troops together with Escumbuit and his Indians and landed them at Placentia, the principal French settlement on Newfoundland. Mr. DeBrouillon, governor of Placentia, had a force of men from this settlement, who were to take part in this action. The island was occupied by the two world powers with the British settlements on the east side of the island.

The British set up their defense of the settlement assuming the attack would come from the sea. As we shall see, this would turn out to be a costly miscalculation.

On the first of November, D'Iberville set out from Placentia with his Canadians and the Indians. After a nine day march in some of the most severe winter conditions, they reached Forillon. On the way, they captured an Englishman, who escaped and warned the English in St. Johns that they were on their way. Mr. DeBrouillon, a vain and power hungry man, worked all his intrigues attempting to take overall command of, not only his men from Platencia, but also the Canadians and Indians under D'Iberville. When DeBrouillon learned that the Canadians and Indians would fight only under D'Iberville's command, he finally agreed to share the glory with D'Iberville. Now the entire army advanced towards Bay de Toulle, which was six leagues from Florillon.

On November 26, after advancing about three leagues, they encountered a force of 30 Englishmen, who immediately retreated to a defensive position from which they offered stiff resistance. During the subsequent fight, the enemy lost six men and the rest abandoned their position and fled to St. Johns.

That evening, when Brouillon and the army arrived, it snowed so heavily that they had to spend the entire next day waiting for it to stop. The hyperactive Montigny, together with Escumbuit and his Indians, made a reconnaissance through the woods and brought back several prisoners.

On the morning of the second day, they began to advance again with Montigny and 30 Canadians leading the way. Behind them followed De Brouillan and D'Iberville with the rest of the troops.[13] The garrison of Placentia led the column, but it was agreed that the Canadians would begin the attack.

After marching about two and a half hours, Montigny spied, within pistol shot, approximately 90 Englishmen positioned behind rocks. A fight broke out immediately in which Montigny and his 20 men held their own until the army came up to support him. De Brouillan and his men then made a frontal assault while D'Iberville with Escumbuit and his Indians circled and flanked the enemy. After about a half hour fight, the English broke and made a fighting retreat towards St. Johns with D'Iberville, the Canadians and Escumbuit's Indians in full pursuit.

St. Johns was only three quarters of a league distant. When the people of St. Johns saw their force of 90 men retreating, they panicked. The English had lost half of their

---

[13] Charlevoix, History of New France, page 43, "On the morning of the 28th, the whole army marched in order, Montigny with thirty other Canadians in the van, five hundred paces ahead of the main body. De Brouillan and d'Iberville followed at the head of the troops, having with them Nescambiouit, an Abenaqui chief, a brave man, who was at Versailles in 1707 caressed and loaded with presents by the king.

men in this action and the survivors now piled into the palisade enclosing the fort.

As the French entered the settlement, they saw a large vessel in the harbor putting on sail to leave. Many of the local residents had carried their most valued possessions aboard ship, putting to sea leaving the remaining inhabitants to their fate.

The French sent a woman prisoner into the fort with the demand that they surrender, but the commander of the fort retained her without sending back an answer. The French, concluding the English were going to defend the fort, sent men back to bring up cannon and mortar which had been left at Bay de Toulle.

On the nights of the 29 and 30, Montigny was ordered to burn the houses outside the fort. D'Iberville and Escumbuit advanced with 30 hand picked men to support them. De Brouillan provided additional cover in the event assistance was needed. On the night of the 30th, in the glare of the burning houses, a soldier came out bearing a white flag. The commander of the fort asked for a meeting outside because he did not want the French to see the deplorable condition of the fort. They had virtually no supplies and the fort was manned mostly by fishermen and other civilians. A group of four met the French outside the fort. Brouillan submitted his terms and the English commander asked if he could deliver his answer the following day. From the height of the Fort, they saw two large English ships tacking to enter the harbor, but the French had also seen them. Brouillan demanded they surrender at once or the assault would begin immediately. Later the two ships, seeing the situation, reversed course and headed back to England.

De Brouillan wanted to occupy and hold the settlement using D'Iberville's Canadians, but D'Iberville refused saying he needed every man for the expeditions he had in view. In the end they agreed to burn the fort and the remaining houses and abandon the settlement.

Montigny and Escumbuit captured most of the small outlying settlements in the area and took more than 700 additional prisoners to Placentia. Only two posts remained to the English. Bonnavista was too well fortified and impossible to reach with siege guns over impossible terrain and Carbonniere Island was unapproachable in winter. Here 300 English retreated to safety.

D'Iberville[14] decided to return to Placentia to wait for the reinforcements needed to capture the two remaining English settlements. After a long wait, Mr. De Serigny arrived May 18, 1697 with orders for D'Iberville to proceed instead to Hudson Bay to fight the English and their Iroquois allies there.

Before leaving, he dispatched a ship down the coast to return Chief Escumbuit and his warriors to their own settlements. Escumbuit respected D'Iberville and he especially admired Montigny, an intrepid warrior in his own im-

---

[14] History of New France by The Rev. P.F.X. de Charlevoix,S.J. (p.47), in the final paragraph of his account of this action writes; "In this campaign D'Iberville gave striking proofs of his ability, and was at every point where danger was to be met or hardship undergone; next to him came Montigny, generally in the van and often leaving little to be done by those who followed him. After them, the most distinguished were Boucher and de la Perriere, d'Amor de Plaine, Duque de Boisbriand, all three Canadian gentlemen, and **Nescambiouit**. There is no doubt, had there been force enough to complete this well-advanced conquest and guard the posts from which the English had been expelled, they would have lost the island of Newfoundland forever; but few men in France then saw how important it was to secure the total possession."

age. He hated to part company with them, but Montigny promised him that they would fight the English and yell the scalping cry together again.

Fort William Henry.

ANDOVER AND HAVERHILL ATTACKED BY INDIANS 1696-1698

Meanwhile, the settlers at York, Wells and Kittery managed to hold their own. War parties of Indians continued to prowl the frontier from the Kennebec to Connecticut. About this time, an event took place that typified the state of the frontier while demonstrating the toughness of the settlers in the face of this reign of terror.

In 1697 the little town of Haverhill on the Merrimac consisted of 30 houses. The village nestled on the bank of the Merrimac and right behind it up on the hill was a small hamlet with a small stream, the Little River, crawling between them. There were three block houses in the village to which the outlying villagers were supposed to flee in case of an attack, but it was not a secure arrangement for those settlers who chose to live up on the hill and away from the protection of the blockhouses.

On March 15, Thomas Duston, a farmer, rode out from his house to inspect one of his fields when he suddenly spied some Indians. He had just left his wife Hannah at home in bed recovering from recent child birth with the neighbor girl Mary Neff to assist her. There were eight children aged two to seventeen in and about the house.

Duston rode hard for the house with the Indians whooping behind him. He managed to gain a little time, but when he arrived at the house, there was not a moment to lose. His wife said she simply could not get out of bed so he made the split-second decision to save as many of the children as he could. He told them to run to the garrison as fast as they could. After failing to get his wife out of bed, he went outside, mounted his horse, and by placing himself between the running children and the Indians, he managed to hold the Indians at bay by brandishing his gun. They fired several shots trying to shoot him off his horse. Smart enough to hold his fire, and with his loaded gun pointed at the Indians, he kept them from making a run at him and the children. On reaching the safety of the garrison, however, they looked back to see their house in flames.

The Indians caught up with Mary Neff trying to flee with the newborn and brought her back to the house. Then they ordered Hannah Duston to get out of bed and get dressed. Knowing that the Indians were going to tomahawk her on the spot unless she obeyed, she managed to do what seemed impossible a moment before. She managed to get on only one shoe before the Indians forced them out of the house and herded them to the north.

The new-born child was slowing them down. When they reached Atkinson, one of the Indians killed it by dashing it against a nearby apple tree. As they were driven unmercifully, other captives, unable to maintain the pace set by the Indians, were dispatched with tomahawks, scalped and left by the side of the trail.

Many of the houses in the little hamlet were burning and 27 settlers lay dead or dying while 13 captives loaded down with loot stolen from their own homes were being driven north. Hannah Duston remembered walking due north for a few days, then heading west until they came to the Merrimac River. That description would agree with the available Indian trails. They probably took the Pentucket trail north to Sandown where they picked up the Massabesic Trail which led along the north shore of Lake Massabesic through what is now the city of Manchester to the Merrimac River. From there they followed the river north to a small island at the mouth of the Contoocook River, now known as Duston Island.

The Indians split into several groups to throw off pursuers, and now they found themselves part of a small party of Indians consisting of two male warriors, three squaws and seven children. With them was a 14-year old boy named Samuel Leonardson, who had been their captive for 18 months. He had learned to speak their language, and, by this time, they considered him one of their own. Within a short time, the Indians planned to head north in their canoes where they expected to sell their prisoners to the French.

Hannah's main captor had formerly lived with a man named Rowlandson in Lancaster. He told her that he learned to pray the English way, but later decided the French way was better. Sometimes this Indian master would taunt them saying, "Why need you trouble yourselves so? If your God will have you delivered, so shall it be."

Finally, they were told by their master that they were leaving the following day and that they were going to have to run the gauntlet at the next Indian village where they planned to stay overnight. That is to say, they would be stripped of their clothing and forced to run between two lines made up of all the men, women and children of the village, who would be free to strike them with clubs, tomahawks and sticks as they made their way through the gauntlet. They terrorized them by describing how some were beaten senseless or killed in the gauntlet.

Hannah Duston was a big woman, but was not fat; she was a big rugged farm woman brought up on the frontier. She would not be considered delicate under any circumstances. She had gotten out of bed when she thought she didn't have the strength to do so. Somehow she managed to keep up on the march when others were being tomahawked and scalped for lagging behind. Distraught by the loss of her baby, she was still determined to survive.

Now, however, she faced two things she felt she couldn't endure. First, there was no way she was going to run naked through an Indian gauntlet; second, she knew that once they departed this camp and headed up river, she would probably never see her husband and eight children again. In her extreme desperation, she made her plan and confided it to Mary Neff and the Leonardson boy. She instructed Samuel to ask one of the Indians what the best place was to strike a victim with a tomahawk in order to kill him instantly and to also find out how victims were scalped. The boy managed to do this without arousing suspicion. Now Hannah explained her plan of action for the night ahead to Mary Neff and young Samuel. She told them that all of the Indians had to be killed to prevent survivors from alerting other nearby Indians. Young Leonardson begged her to spare one young Indian boy with whom he was friendly. She agreed to this single exception.

Various reasons have been given for the lack of caution by the Indians. Most say that the Indians considered the boy one of them after 18 months of captivity, and that the cowed women seemed to present no danger to the Indians. Others suggested that perhaps the two male braves had been drinking. For whatever reason, they all bedded down for the night with no restraints on the prisoners.

When all was silent in the camp, the three conspirators rose. Silently picking up tomahawks, they stood over their victims. At Hannah's signal, they struck hard and fast. Hannah buried her tomahawk in the head of her captor and the Leonardson boy slew the Indian from whom he had learned the killing technique. Striking rapidly they killed all but one squaw who was severely wounded, but managed to escape into the underbrush. The Indian boy they had agreed to spare escaped with her.

They went to the canoes and sunk all but the one in which they set out in the river to make their escape. Hardly afloat, Hannah suddenly realized that the only way she could prove what they had done would be to bring the scalps of their victims with them. Returning to shore, she took the scalps of the dead Indians and wrapped them in a piece of linen that had been looted from her own home.

They were still in peril! Not only did they have to worry about pursuit from the Indians, they had the river to navigate. They had to negotiate various rapids and shallows and had to be constantly alert to hear the roar of falls ahead in order to beach the canoe and carry it below the falls to calmer water. They had to portage the canoe around the falls not only in Manchester, New Hampshire, but also down river to Lowell and Lawrence, Massachusetts. Finally, half starved, they arrived back in Haverhill, where they were greeted as people returned from the dead.

The news of Hannah Duston's feat swept through the colonies like wild fire. Even the French historians write of her ordeal in awe, describing her as the English Amazon.

She and her companions went to Boston, where she displayed the scalps to the Massachusetts General Court. She was given a reward of 25 pounds and Mary Neff and Samuel Leonardson were each awarded ten pounds, ten shillings. The Governor of Maryland sent her a congratulatory letter and a pewter tankard which is still on display at the Haverhill Historical Society. Monuments still stand in Haverhill, and in Boscowen, New Hampshire honoring the memory of this heroic woman.

Many of the Duston family relics are on display at the Haverhill Historical Society including Hannah Duston's hand written testament crediting God's intervention in her miraculous deliverance from captivity.

An interesting sidelight to Hannah Duston's sudden burst of religious fervor, which came after her return to Haverhill, bears mention.

After her return, she was reluctant to claim her bounty for the Indian scalps she had brought back. She was very afraid she might be punished for killing the Indians. She had been closely questioned about her miraculous return by a famous Puritan preacher named Cotton Mather. He sternly warned her that it was time she mended her ways and that it was her duty to credit her deliverance to the will of God. She complied by writing the testament now displayed in the Haverhill Historical Society.

She had a sister who had borne a child out of wedlock and the baby had died at birth. This same sister had a second child in the same circumstances which also died. During this era, the law required that a woman in these circumstances must prove that the child had died of natural causes. One wonders how a simple farm girl would be able to prove to a court room full of learned jurors that her new born had died of natural causes. In her case, the Reverend Cotton Mather, famous Puritan fire and brimstone preacher, brought her before the court and saw to it that she was hanged! Little wonder that Hannah was afraid to report what she had done. (Mary Dyer, of course, was the first woman hanged in Boston).

Many people of his era disliked Cotton Mather. He was considered to be pompous and self-important. Today he might be nicknamed *Cotton Blather*, but in the days of the Puritans, no one dared to oppose him.

Penhallow, who wrote the best known history of the 1703-1713 period, had a very poor opinion of Mather. It is from Penhallow we get a vivid, perhaps prejudiced, picture of the settlers' war with the Indians during that ten year period.

Unknown to the people of New England, during the winter of 1696-97, the French were planning a blow which, in its scope and audacity, would have made the Indian border raids pale by comparison. Louis XIV directed almost every military move of his royal colony from his palace at Versailles. For years he was of the opinion that the only thing which would leave his Royal Canadian Colony in peace would be to invade and put Boston to ashes.

At the ports of Brest and Rochefort, 13 heavy ships plus two fire boats were fitted out for a raid on Boston. With the Marquis de Nesmond in command, they sailed for Newfoundland with orders to defeat the British Squadron which was supposed to be there. From there he sailed to the Penobscot where he met 1,500 troops from Canada and several hundred Abenaki warriors for an attack on

Boston. Several Frenchmen, during their captivity in Boston, had the freedom to survey and make accurate maps of the town.

Twelve hundred troops with their artillery were to be landed at Dorchester to force the barrier across the neck of the peninsula which divided it from Boston. At the same time, Saint Castin was to land at Noddle's Island with a troop of Canadians and all the Indians. From there they planned to go over to Charlestown by canoe, and after subduing that community, move on to Boston which could then be attacked from both the south and the north. Meanwhile, 200 men were to seize the battery at Castle Island and then land in their canoes near Long Wharf under the guns of the fleet.

At that time, Boston had about 7,000 inhabitants, but many of the men were normally at sea, fishing or whaling. The French believed the available defenders probably didn't number more than 800. After destroying everything in Boston, they planned to march north to Salem looting and carrying everything of value on the way. From Salem they planned to march up the coast to Portsmouth, New Hampshire covered in their line of march by their fleet of war ships.

Count Frontenac, Canadian Governor, though 77 years old, planned to lead the land forces. By June 1696, with his forces ready, he awaited word from his fleet commander. Nesmond finally sent word that he was delayed by head winds and had only 50 days provisions. The grandiose plan thus came to nothing and the venture was abandoned never to be mounted again.

In early 1697 a ship arrived in Quebec bearing the news that the Treaty of Ryswick had been signed on the continent and England and France were once again at peace. In modern wars, hostilities cease immediately when news of an armistice is flashed around the world. Not so in the late 1600's.

In early 1697, unaware of the peace treaty, D'Iberville, the Sieur de Montigny, and Escumbuit were completing their conquest of the French settlements in St. Johns. In March, Haverhill was raided by a band of Indians and Hannah Duston had been carried into captivity. But up in what is now known as Fryeburg, Maine, Chief Escumbuit was planning to take his revenge on Pasco Chubb, safely retired from the military and now living in Andover, Massachusetts.

The French learned that Chubb was tried and sent to jail for his failure to defend the English fort of Pemequid. They also knew that he was released after a few months and was living in Andover. The French officers showed Escumbuit the location on their map and he noted that the trail that would lead him to Chubb carried him close to the camp of a small band of Indians with whom he had stayed during previous raids on the settlements. He knew nothing of the peace treaty between the French and the English; he knew only that the Abenaki Indians were still at war with the English, and that he had a personal score to settle with Pasco Chubb.

Following standard Indian procedures, he asked for a meeting of the Chief's Council, and, when it came his turn, he spoke at length about the havoc their own Pigwacket braves had inflicted on the English at Pemequid and in Newfoundland. He had lost only four of the 40 warriors who went on this campaign with him, and the survivors had all returned loaded down with loot taken from the houses of the settlements. The village celebrated the victory with feasting, dancing and singing. The returning warriors spread the word about Escumbuit and how great his image had become with their French masters. They described how the War Chiefs of the Penobscot, the Kennebec, the Adroscoggin and the Micmac showed their jealousy over the special attention given to Escumbuit by the French commanders. They told how the Frenchmen vied to have Escumbuit and his warriors at their side when the fighting began. Of course, his meant that those warriors who fought with Escumbuit also drew the admiration of the French. As the home town fans of the star athlete basked in the glow of his fame, so did the older chiefs of the tribe beam with pride over his accomplishments.

He described in great detail how Chubb had lulled the Indians into a sense of false security by his friendly demeanor and his liberal servings of the white man's *firewater*, all under the guise of creating a friendly atmosphere for the discussion of the prisoner exchange. The temper of the council mounted as he described how the Indian chiefs, Egeremet and Abenquid, were slaughtered at the onset of the surprise attack. Of the 12 Indians present, only he, Chief Taxous and a few of their braves had escaped, leaving behind their dead and imprisoned comrades. He concluded by describing the condition of the Indian captive chained, and almost dead in a dungeon after the surrender of the fort. The chiefs could not understand why the French had not allowed him to take his revenge on Chubb and the other captives. Escumbuit told them that the ways of the white man were very strange and could not always be explained to please the Indians.

When he asked for an affirmative vote on his plan to avenge Chubb's treacherous action, all hands were raised in support of his plan. The council agreed that, in spite of their strong desire to take Chubb's scalp, it would be better to make a surprise attack in the dead of winter when the settlers pulled back their militia patrols.

It had been a long, hard campaign in the dead of winter for Escumbuit and his warriors. They deserved a break after the rigors of Newfoundland and they took it. They joined their tribesmen in preparations for their annual move to the sea coast. Visions of lobster, shell fish and seal hunting filled their mind as well as the prospect of trading for English rum. Soon, thoughts of the coming winter raid on Andover were pushed aside as they quickly made the transition from warrior to the more sedate pace of village life. Not so with Escumbuit. He was making plans for a side trip down to the lake at Hampstead, where the local Indians could help him plan for his winter raid on Andover.

The summer passed quickly, and Escumbuit managed to relax and enjoy the respect of his fellow tribesmen. He even played Indian lacrosse in a makeshift field set up on one of the sandy beaches. As he gorged himself on the bounty of the sea, he quickly gained back the 15 pounds he lost during the hard and harsh winter. He particularly enjoyed the indolent days spent lounging by the bay in the sun, smoking and enjoying the idle talk of his fellow braves.

His relationship with his wife was matter-of-fact. He no longer expected her to bear him a son, and although his wife performed her wifely duty at his pleasure, the passion had gone out of their marriage. Yet, he did not yearn for other women for he was a loner, and he existed in his own independent shell. He still missed Moosu, his boy-hood friend as well as Montigny, who had the potential of filling the same role in Escumbuit's life as had Moosu. He was moody and the members of his tribe had learned long since to let him be, and even gave up trying to extract the secret of his silver mine from him.

He made his trip down to Hampstead with another warrior and they stayed on the big island as welcome guests of the 50 displaced Indians who lived there. Joseph, a displaced member of the Wampanaug tribe of Massachsetts, knew the Town of Andover well, and he had in fact taken his English name at the urging of a Puritan preacher who had tried in vain to convert him to Christianity. Lt. Colonel Dudley Bradstreet,[15] member of the militia and a local magistrate, helped him in his past. His appetite for loot outweighed his loyalty to Bradstreet, and he agreed to guide Escumbuit's war party to Pasco Chubb's house located in the north section of Andover. His one stipulation was that Bradstreet and his family be spared. He wanted to share in the plunder taken from the Bradstreet's home, however. Having been treated well by the Colonel's family, he wanted them left unharmed. After some thought, Escumbuit agreed to his terms concluding that his principal target was, after all, Pasco Chubb.

---

[15] Historical Sketches Of Andover, Sarah Loring Bailey, (p.130), Lt. Colonel Bradstreet was the son of Simon and Anne Bradstreet, among the best known early settlers of the Town of Andover. He was a mill owner on the Merrimac river and she became famous as "America's first woman poet." Among her descendants are Oliver Wendell Holmes and Wendell Phillips. Dudley Bradstreet was a town selectman, a magistrate and a member of the militia.

The guide confirmed that there were about a dozen places in the Merrimac between Andover and Haverhill which could be forded by men afoot, but the constant English patrols along the south bank of the River endangered a summer attack. A surprise attack over the frozen Merrimac in the dead of winter had better prospects for success.

Escumbuit returned to the Biddeford area to rejoin his tribe; his anxiety eased by the sure knowledge that he had a plan which would safely provide him with his long awaited confrontation with the hated Chubb.

The tribe reluctantly abandoned the summer camp at Biddeford and paddled up the Saco River to their winter home in Fryeburg. The Chief made a lonely trip to his mine and came back with a canoe-load of ore which he used to make musket balls and lead sinkers. This was how he passed his time until the snows came and the tribe began to prepare for their winter hunt.

The snow came early and all the braves were out on their snow shoes hunting deer and moose in January. When the tribe was assured of a meat supply for the rest of the winter, Escumbuit finally called on his 30 volunteers to make themselves ready for their trip.

These warriors survived worse conditions in Newfoundland the previous winter. Well-provisioned with pemmican and parched corn, the party set a course south walking over the frozen ice of the Saco River. They each carried a musket and the ever present tomahawk or war-club. In the Ogunquit area they took the Nesowakik trail down to Rollingsford where they stayed two nights at the Quamphegan Indian village. From there they followed the Pentucket trail to Exeter where they headed west on the Squanscott trail to the Chester area, and picked up the Pawtucket trail which brought them down into Hampstead.

At the north end of the lake they crossed a frozen swampy area to the large island which was the home of a mixed band of Indians, refugees from local Indian tribes, driven out of their tribal homes by the encroaching settlers. Some of these Indians, yielding to the pressure of the English settlers moving up the Merrimac, had left for the Canadian mission village at St. Francis. Finding the Canadian climate too harsh, they returned to this remote lake which offered everything they had been accustomed to in the Merrimac Valley. Here, they hoped to be left in peace.

Their neutrality did not lessen their hatred for the English, and they saw little danger in harboring this war party for a couple of nights. Escumbuit and his braves were entertained with typical Indian hospitality. By now Escumbuit's exploits were known to all the Abenakis and this small tribe was honored by his visit. Some of the young, local braves wanted to join the raid, but the local Chief, fearing reprisal by the settlers, was adamant; they were to remain in camp except for the one guide who knew Colonel Bradstreet.

Escumbuit agreed to leave his totemic sign at the scene to serve notice that it was he, the Pigwacket Chief from the headwaters of the Saco River, who led the raid. He agreed to head north via Haverhill after the raid to divert attention away from the Indians at Big Island Pond. Here they were delayed another day by a howling blizzard. They passed the time in a crowded long house, smoking, eating, and telling stories

Well rested, the raiding party set out on the morning of February 21, 1698, and followed their guide over local trails which brought them to the north bank of the Merrimac River in the area of the line which now separates the City of Lawrence, Massachusetts and the Town of Methuen. The northeastern end of the Town of Andover now lay directly on the opposite bank of the frozen river; this area is now the incorporated village of North Andover. They had traveled on snow shoes over dry powdery snow and it was fiercely cold. There being no dwelling in sight on the opposite bank, they risked two small fires using dry wood which did not give off any smoke. There they huddled together, eating pemmican and parched corn, and tried to catch some sleep wrapped in their heavy bear skins, wolf skins, and trade blankets.

Next day,[16] at about 2 in the morning, Escumbuit strapped on his snow shoes and led his 30 warriors out onto the frozen ice which provided a base for 18 inches of new powder snow.

With the storm abating, and the wind dying, the full moon illuminated an eerie scene of 30 braves advancing through the snow in line. Any chance observer on the opposite bank would have seen them coming, but this was not a night to leave the shelter of a warm house. The Indians, raised in these conditions in northern Maine, were used to the sub-zero temperature, and they seemed to glide through the snow; the only warning of their coming: the soft shuffle of their snow shoes as they moved

---

[16] Authors note: There is some confusion over the date of the raid. In "Andover: Symbol of New England," the author, Claude M Fuess uses March 4, 1698 and Sarah Loring Bailey, in her "Historical Sketches Of Andover" uses both February 22nd and March 4, 1698. There seems to be agreement that it had been the harshest winter in memory. Both agree on the general details of the raid and that Assacumbuit led the party of 30 Indians.

towards their objective. When they reached the south shore of the river, Joseph took the lead. Arriving at Chubb's house, Escumbuit held nine of the Indians there with him while Joseph led the remainder to the Bradstreet residence. Ten Indians were positioned there after which Joseph and the other nine warriors sought out another nearby home. On Escumbuit's orders, they were to attack simultaneously when Escumbuit discharged a musket at dawn.

By 4 AM, Escumbuit and his party lay concealed behind one of the outbuildings of Chubb's home less than 40 yards from the house. The Chubbs would spend the final hours of their life secure in their warm bed, unaware that the Indians crouched mere yards away waiting for daybreak.

Andover suffered a great deal of turmoil during 1690-8, having experienced their share of hit and run attacks by marauding Indians. There were a dozen places on the river between Andover and Haverhill which could be forded and from where they could launch a surprise attack at any time. As recently as 1696, John Hoyt of Amesbury and a young man named Peters had been slain on the road to Haverhill. The situation had the town in a constant state of tension. Added to this was the "Great Andover Witch Hunt".[17]

---

[17] Andover: Symbol Of New England, by Claude M. Feuss, (p. 79,-81)," During the spring and summer of 1692, at a moment when Andover people were still much concerned over possible attacks by hostile savages, they were harassed from another quarter by enemies both more insidious and more dangerous. In the words of Marion L. Sterkey, the Devil took over Andover, and the village was paralyzed with terror. The story of how a neurotic, irresponsible group of chil-

(Even Bradstreet and his wife were forced to flee the town for a period to escape the fury of those who believed *him* to be guilty of witchcraft. He was the sole, sane voice to stand for a poor woman coerced into admitting to being a witch; for this, he in turn was accused of practicing the black craft and having caused the death of nine people. Such was the extent of the madness that enveloped the town.)

Now, as if the victim of some giant conspiracy, the town was cursed by the arrival of Pasco Chubb, an unprincipled man, and the town was about to be the theater for, and to share in, his ruin.

As the sky brightened on the glistening white landscape, a musket shot startled the frigid, dry air, causing the Indians to storm the three targeted houses. They ap-

---

dren corrupted a supposedly mature and religious society is the saddest chapter in the annals of the town. For a few weeks the community was permeated, even dominated, by suspicion. At the crisis of the delusion, the worst and the best, the old and the young, might at any hour be charged with witchcraft and convicted on the most preposterous evidence. Nobody could tell who would be the next victim. If we believe the sworn testimony, warlocks and witches rode the air on broomsticks; strange apparitions desecrated marshes and meadows; unholy rights of baptism and dedication were celebrated; innocent men and women were marked and plagued with degrading symbols. Indeed all hell broke loose, and hate, with its twin emotion, fear, seized and held possession of even the most pious churchgoers. It was as if something morbid and repressed had been suddenly released to run its devastating course."

Page 82, "The witchcraft delusion is still associated with Salem, a city which had little to do with the course of events except to provide the town hall where some of the trials took place and the gallows where a few of the victims were executed. Indeed in some respects the consequences of the hysteria at Andover were even more incredible than they were at Salem Village."

plied the greasy black, white and ochre war paint to each other's face. Like creatures from hell, they burst into the houses, rousing the still sleeping inhabitants.

Escumbuit and his party used a log as a battering ram to explode the back door of Chubb's house off its hinges. Chubb met them in his night-gown half-way down the stairs from the second floor as he headed for his musket. He turned quickly to run back to his bedroom, but a bullet was quicker, dropping him on the threshold of the second floor. Escumbuit was on him in a flash. All Pasco Chubb felt was the searing burn as the musket ball entering his back and then, the war club fell: an explosion of light followed by a black void. His wife's death was merciful only in its swiftness. The poor woman, bound to her husband by vows, but not by his stained past, alas, suffered the same fate.

The Indians quickly took the scalps and immediately began to loot the house. They soon realized that there was not much worth taking; the Chubb family was not prosperous. Firing the house was easy; they simply knocked over the banked hardwood fire in the living room stove, and as the flames surged up the wall of the living room, they abandoned the house carrying fire brands to put the adjacent barn to the torch. After putting a halter and saddle on the only horse in the barn, they led him outside and set fire to the barn. Now, they headed for the Bradstreet residence, where they expected to have better luck with their looting.

When the attack began, Escumbuit led the assault on the Chubb house in order to wreak his personal revenge on the hated Pasco Chubb. Joseph, their guide, was in the third group which had by-passed the Bradstreet house to attack another nearby. He didn't want to be part of the attack on the Colonel's house. The ten Indians, who had burst into the Bradstreet house, surprised the occupants in their beds. They tomahawked and scalped Major Wade, a relative visiting with them from Mystic, but spared Bradstreet and his wife. After commanding them to dress, they led them outside and apparently were planning to take them captive. They led them about 50 yards from the house when suddenly Escumbuit arrived and ordered their release. Colonel Bradstreet's previous kind treatment of Joseph had earned him and his a wife a reprieve from either death or captivity by the Indians.

Cotton Mather, in his *Magnalia*, was reluctant to concede the quality of mercy to the Indians, noting; "In the midst of their fury there was one piece of mercy the like whereof had never been seen before; for they had got Colonel Dudley Bradstreet into their hands, but perceiving the town mustering to follow them, their hearts were so changed that they dismissed their captives without any further damage unto their persons."

By this time the third party of raiders set two more houses on fire and murdered two more people. A general melee followed in the course of which they took two more horses and either burned or took off with many of the town records. About 20 heads of cattle and a large store of corn were burned in one barn. They also removed and burned some pulpit cushions from the church. Finally, noting signs of the town militia mustering to meet the threat, they took off with what loot they could carry and headed over the Haverhill road for that city. The militia was not equipped with snow shoes and it was futile for them to mount a pursuit as Escumbuit and his warriors prepared for the winter conditions, quickly outdistanced them.

In the outskirts of Haverhill, they encountered Jonathan Haines, Samuel Ladd and their two sons. They killed and scalped the elders and took the boys captive. The younger Haines boy, however, managed to escape--the second time he had escaped Indian captors in two years. They also invaded and burned the house of Mr. Timothy Johnson and killed his 19-year-old daughter Penelope.

They skirted the village of Haverhill and headed north on the Pentucket Trail to Hampstead, where Joseph parted company with them, leading one of the horses loaded with loot. Escumbuit and his braves then set out on the long return trip to their village up the Saco River. Historical accounts confirm that it was Assacumbuit, also known as Escumbuit to the English, who had led the war party.[18]

Although the home of Dudley and Anne Bradstreet eventually burned, their name still lives in town history. The land on which Andover was incorporated was purchased from the Sagamore Cutshamache for six pounds and a coat. Simon Bradstreet moved his family to the area from Ipswich in 1644 and he contructed the first mill on the Cochechevicke near its junction with the Merrimac River. This area became the center for the manufacturing industries of Lawrence as well as for the Sutton and Stevens Mills in what later became the separate community of North Andover.

This 1698 attack was the last and most severe on Andover, but the inhabitants felt the danger was far from

---

[18] Historical Sketches Of Andover, by Sarah Loring Bailey, (p.181) "All the facts go to indicate that it was a deliberate act of Indian revenge. The attack was led by the fierce and implacable foe of the whites, Assacumbuit."

over. They built two block houses on the river well equipped with munitions, and provided the militia with snow shoes which enabled them to make winter patrols. They never lost another citizen to the Indians from this date forward. Clearly, Pasco Chubb's betrayal of the Indians at Pemequid Point, was at the root of the Indian reprisal; other innocent residents of Andover had the misfortune of being his neighbor.[19]

---

[19] Andover; Symbol Of New England, by Claude M. Fuess, (p.76) The story has the neat and inevitable conclusion of a Greek tragedy, in which Character is Destiny. On February 22, 1698, a large band of Indians, led by Assacumbuit, one of their most energetic and daring chieftains, made a carefully planned attack on Andover. Because the winter was the most severe within the memories of living habitants, the invasion was apparently unexpected.

Merrimac River: Indian attack on Andover.

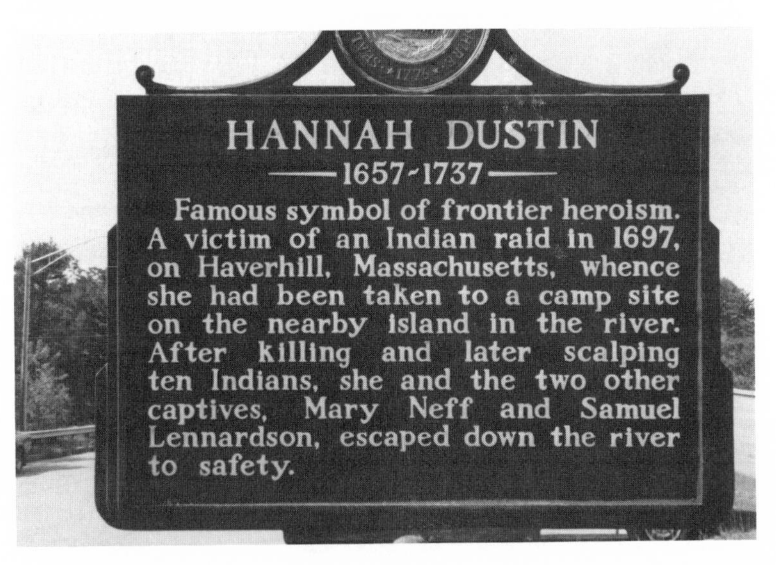

Top: Statue of Hannah Dustin, Haverhill, Massachusetts. Bottom: Commemorative Plaque on Hannah Dustin, Boscawen, New Hampshire. (Spelling is also *Dustin*).

LOVEWELL AND THE PIGWACKETS LAST STAND 1725

Captain John Newsholme left Great Bay in June. Now, in September, the days were getting shorter, and the cold winds were beginning to sweep in from the northwest stripping the autumn color burst of leaves to the ground. Most of Chief Escumbuit's small band returned to Big Island Pond in August to harvest the corn and pick blueberries. After this important project was completed, they returned to Great Bay to finish their season. The harvested corn was hung in the wigwams and the longhouse to dry for the winter. The blueberries were laid out on pieces of bark in the sun to dry.

The dry corn would be ground and used in a variety of ways during the winter, and the dried blueberries were mixed with bits of dried meat, crushed nuts and pigeon fat to make the pemmican the braves would take with them during their winter hunts. The pumpkins were left on the vines until the tribe returned in late September. Then the pumpkins and squash would be harvested and cut into strips to be dried and stored for use in soups and stews during the winter.

They returned to Great Bay the end of August and would spend another month enjoying the bounty of the coastal marshes and inlets. There were plenty of water fowl making their annual migration south to be netted and shot. Lobsters, clams and oysters were still plentiful as were the porpoise, fish and seal. Now, oysters were gathered to be dried and smoked on racks high above the flames of their camp fires to be taken back to the lake for later use.

Chief Escumbuit stayed at the summer camp on the shore of Great Bay with the older braves and squaws who minded those children too young to help with the harvest back at the lake. He went out each day in a canoe to fish, but the exertion of paddling seemed to tire him. The many winters spent in wigwams or in the longhouse where cooking fires burned constantly was taking its toll on his health. Like most Indians, he had smoked a pipe since boyhood, and this too had taken its toll on his lungs. Already old by Indian standards, he never connected the constant inhalation of smoke with his shortness of breath.

In the middle of September, he was anticipating the return of Captain John Newsholm in his 40-foot yawl. He had used up the last of his rum, but knew the Captain would soon replenish his supply. This, more than news of the trading post in Rollingsford, was what occupied his thinking. When one of the young boys of the tribe sighted the sail of the Captain's boat far down the bay, the Chief waited with his usual stoicism.

The yawl finally dropped anchor well out beyond the low tide mark, but he still waited patiently for Newsholm to send word to him. Finally, two young children came to tell him that the Captain wanted them to bring him out in their canoe.

Once aboard, the Captain greeted him warmly pulling up a deck chair for him and sending his deck hand with his key to draw two tots of rum. With a couple of fingers of rum in his belly and his pipe lit, the Captain came directly to the point.

"Chief, I thought to have good news for you about the trading post, but the council refused my petition. They asked if I had a partner in my scheme and I told them no, but they didn't believe me. Seems like one of their members had kin that got scalped at Fort Loyal, and when he heard you were going to be my partner, he soured the others on my deal. Now, you might rightly ask--how did he know you were connected to the deal? You remember the Micmac deck hand I had with me last trip? He got drunk in port and spilled his guts to one of the English for the price of a bottle of rum. For that I gave him a whipping and sent him off my ship, but the harm's done."

Chief Escumbuit listened impassively with no display of emotion as the Captain continued.

"But I've got news that might concern your silver mine. The English grow bolder every day. They have raised the bounty again for Indian scalps. One day all the Abenaki will go north to join their brothers in St. Francis. I know of your feud with the Pigwackets and why you hide from them. The English want to know where you are, but I am John Newsholm and I do not betray my friends. One day you will show me your mine and we will both be rich."

With no outward display of emotion, Chief Escumbuit accepted the news impassively, thinking, "I am a Pigwacket War Chief. I trust this pale face, but still he must not see my disappointment." Then, speaking aloud, he said, "John Newsholm, you are as a brother to me. I hear you speak and I trust your words. I understand the white man's hate. Like my Pigwacket enemies, they too seek my scalp. But hear me speak. I know the pale face will triumph one day over the Indians. Then the Pigwacket will live in Canada with the French. When that day comes and the treaty of peace is signed by the English, I will go with you to my mine and show you the silver. Until then, we must remain friends."

Just four months earlier, unknown to Newsholm and Escumbuit, on May 7, 1725, an important battle had taken place near the site of the Pigwacket village in the area we now know as Fryeburg, Maine. The Captain's prediction about the Pigwacket tribe being forced to leave their home had already come true. A historic fight between John Lovewell's rangers and the Pigwackets led by Chief Paugus took place at Saco lake. The Pigwackets had indeed abandoned their ancestral land and gone to St. Francis. The Captain heard the news of this important battle on returning to Boston in late October, but it would not be until the spring of the following year that he would be able to confirm that the Pigwackets had gone. The history of how Saco Pond came to be known as Lovewell Pond is described in many books and poems and the site of the final fight is marked by a commemorative stone for the casual tourist. It is an important milestone in the history of the pacification of the Abenaki Indians.

John Lovewell's father was an Indian fighter before him, having taken part in the famous Narraganset swamp fight which ended in the death of Chief Metacomen, the Wampenaug Indian, also known as King Philip. The 32-year old Lovewell lived in Dunstable on a 200 acre farm with his wife and two children. A band of Indians attacked Dunstable in the fall of 1724 and carried off two men. The ten men who pursued them were ambushed by the same Indians and most killed in the ambuscade.

Soon after John Lovewell and two other men petitioned the House Of Representatives in Boston for financial assistance for their plan to spend a year hunting Indians. They were awarded a stipend equivalent to about one English shilling per day for their maintenance and they were promised substantial rewards for Indian scalps. Although they are described by some writers as rangers, they were in reality bounty hunters.

A group of 30 men left in November of 1724 and returned in January with one prisoner and one scalp. They had more success on their second trip during which they hiked up the frozen Merrimac River and into the White Mountains on snow shoes. The 87 men were close to starvation until they killed a moose. Lovewell sent part of the party home for lack of food.

Then, in the snow-laden solitude of the winter woods, they spotted a single spire of smoke. It was a party of ten Indians from Canada making their way south to prey on the border villages. The rangers crept close to a single wigwam occupied by Indians, their snow shoes muffling the sound of their approach. Their first volley of musket fire killed all ten. They returned to Dunstable with the ten scalps and the new muskets and blankets given to the Indians by their French sponsors. Flushed with success, they immediately began to plan for their third and fateful trip.

By the middle of April, Lovewell signed on 46 men plus two officers named Farwell and Robbins. Two other members of the band deserve mention. One was an ensign named Seth Wyman of Woburn, the other 21 year old Jonathan Frye of Andover, the Chaplain. A graduate of Harvard University, presently he was a student of theology. Though Chaplain of the party, he carried a musket, hatchet and knife like the others, and no one in the party was more prompt to use his weapons. Starting out on April 15, they had to send one of their group back when he began to suffer from the effects of a previous gunshot wound. Another man was sent with him reducing the available force to 44.

When they reached the west shore of Lake Ossipee, another man fell seriously ill. They built a small log cabin protected by a log palisade and decided to leave their surgeon with him together with Sergeant Woods and seven men. The remaining 34 men marched northeast with the savage snow-clad heights of the White Mountains looming over bare forests to their left.

On the night of May 7, as they lay in the woods near the northeast end of what is now known as Lovewell Pond, the guard thought he heard sounds of men prowling about them. At daybreak, as the Chaplain led them in prayers, they heard a distant shot and soon after they sighted an Indian at a considerable distance on the shore of the lake. Lovewell was wary of being lured into an ambush and asked the men how they felt about it. They were all for pushing forward to investigate. At the time they were in a pine forest near a small brook. Then Lovewell committed a grave error. He ordered them to lay down their packs and moved forward cautiously. After advancing some distance, they were suddenly confronted at close range by the Indian they had seen at a distance. He fired a round of "beaver shot" and some of the pellets struck Lovewell in the stomach and another man received part of the spread. Seth Wyman returned fire and killed the Indian whereupon young Frye, the Chaplain, scalped him with the help of a companion. Lovewell, although believed to be mortally wounded, was able to walk and he ordered them to retrace their advance of about a mile and a half to the pine forest where they had left their packs.

A large party of Indians returning from a trip on the Saco River heard the shots and their investigation turned up the abandoned packs of the rangers. Recognizing an ideal opportunity for an ambush, they concealed themselves and waited for the rangers to return for their packs. Various writers estimate their number at 45 to 80 warriors. By this time, the Indian's store of fighting braves was sadly depleted.

Lovewell and his men returned to find their packs gone. Suddenly from the front and the rear, they took a fusillade of shots and the Indians fell upon them with frightening war cries firing as they advanced. Lovewell received a mortal wound, but managed to fire his musket again while he lay dying. His Lieutenants, Farwell and Robbins, were also badly wounded. Benjamin Hassell of Dunstable cut and ran in the first onslaught taking off alone for the fort at Ossipee. Eight others fell, but the rest fought so hard that they drove the Indians back to cover.

The Indians, for their part, also committed a bad tactical error. Although they set up the ambush perfectly, they split themselves into two groups. The first let the rangers come through their position unmolested. So, when the assault began, they had the rangers trapped front and rear between two groups of Indians. Had they held their position with their superior numbers, they could have eventually wiped out the trapped rangers. By rushing the rangers, they exposed themselves and took fearful casualties in their opening assault.

Lovewell and his two Lieutenants were out of action and the situation was desperate. What saved the entire party from complete destruction was the action of their young ensign, Seth Wyman, who had escaped injury. He led the survivors in a fighting retreat to the shore of the pond, where, with the brook protecting their right flank, they could not be surrounded.

Thus began what some historians describe as *the marathon*. The fight began at ten o'clock in the morning and lasted until nightfall, fighting in a dark pine forest and using the trunks of trees and bushes for concealment. The Indians whooped and yelled their war cries while the rangers answered with shouts and cheers. In a bizarre aspect to the fight, some of the fighters on each side knew each other and they now began to shout threats and insults at each other.

The famous Chief Paugus knew John Chamberlain through their contact during peacetime and they yelled back and forth to each other. With Paugus were his Lieutenants, Wahwa and Adeawando, another Sachem. Ironically, when they needed him most, their legendary Chief Escumbuit was not fighting with them, having been driven from the tribe. He was down at Big Island Pond preparing for his summer at Great Bay.

At one point in the fight, the Indians ceased firing and retreated back into the forest where they could be heard conducting some sort of powwow with a lot of chanting and incantation. They were evidently conducting a sort of pep-rally in an effort to exhort their spirits to help them in their battle with the white men. The intrepid Seth Wyman crept forward to a high position and shot the brave who was leading the chant. Coming at a spiritual ceremony, this bad omen seriously undermined the morale of the Indians.

As the fighting resumed, another incident took place involving Chamberlain and Chief Paugus. Both crept down to the shore of the pond for the purpose of cleaning muskets fouled by excessive firing. Having cleaned and assembled their muskets and in the process of reloading, they spotted one another at the same instant.

History records Chief Paugus saying, "Me kill you quick."

Chamberlain's cool response: "Maybe not." Chamberlain's musket had a large *touch hole* which allowed him to shake powder directly into the pan. Finishing an instant before Paugus, he shot the Chief dead as the Chief's shot flew harmlessly over his head.

(Months later, the son of Paugus went down to Chamberlain's house in Massachusetts to take revenge for his father's death. Looking out his front window Chamberlain spotted the young assassin and shot and killed him with the same musket with which he had killed the boy's father.)

After the sun set, the Indians withdrew, not even attempting to get to the dead rangers to take their scalps. It is estimated that as few as 20 Indians left the field of battle. The rangers had nine of their number killed in the initial ambush. The young chaplain, Frye, was severely wounded about the middle of the afternoon and lay murmuring prayers for his comrades in an audible voice throughout the afternoon.

Solomon Keyes of Billerica continued to fire on the enemy after being wounded twice. After a third wound, he crawled up to ensign Seth Wyman and said, "I'm a dead man, but the Indians ain't gonna get my scalp if I can help it." Crawling along the shore of the pond, he chanced upon a canoe. Managing to push it afloat, he rolled himself into it. With the help of a breeze, he crossed to the opposite shore. (We will hear more of him later.)

Exhausted from the strain of nerves stretched to the limit from the long fight, their food and packs gone, the rangers began to take stock of their plight. Jacob Farrar lay dying on the shore of the pond; Robert Usher and Lieutenant Robbins were unable to move. Of the 34 men, 9 escaped without serious injury, 11 were seriously wounded and the rest were dead or dying except for the one deserter.

About midnight, they decided to make their way back to the fort they had built on the shore of Lake Ossipee. Robbins, unable to move, told them to leave him, adding "The Indians will come to take my scalp in the morning. Load my gun and I'll try to kill another of 'em if I can."

They loaded his gun and left him. Now, they began their nightmarish retreat in the dark of the forest. After struggling for a mile, Farewell, Fry, Josiah Jones and Eleazer Davis--all wounded, were unable to continue. They agreed to stay and wait to be rescued by the men left at the fort.

The remaining 12 men broke up into three smaller groups to reduce the chance of being seen by the Indians, and headed for Ossipee. One of these groups was tracked for some time by the Indians and Elias Barron became separated from his group and was never seen again. When the surviving 11 men reached their small fort in Ossipee, they found it empty. A small amount of pork and bread was left, but the occupants had vanished. The deserter, Hassel, on his arrival several hours earlier, had painted such a stark picture of the entire expedition being wiped out that the men had decided to return to Dunstable on their own, leaving a note on a piece of bark indicating that the rest of the party was killed.

Now, these survivors were joined by Solomon Keyes, the thrice wounded man, who had cast himself adrift in the canoe. When the wind blew him ashore, he found himself stronger and able to manage his way back.

Meanwhile, Frye, Farwell and their two companions found strength to continue to move on but, after a short spell, Frye lay down begging the others to go on without him, saying, "Tell my father that I expect in a few hours to be in eternity and that I am not afraid to die."

Of the remaining three, Farwell died of exhaustion. After wandering 11 days, Davis reached the fort in Ossipee, where he found a small amount of food. He managed to reach Berwick, Maine on his own, arriving there the 27. Jones, after 14 days in the woods, subsisting on tree bark, finally made it to Biddeford in very bad condition.

The others arrived in Dunstable in two parties, 11 men on May 13, and 4 weaker ones shepherded by ensign Seth Wyman on the 15th. Thus, of the 46 men who had left Dunstable in late January, only 17 returned. The Governor gave orders to the militia to proceed with all possible speed to the site of the battle to rescue any survivors and to attack any Indians still there. On arriving, they buried the bodies of Lovewell, Robbins and 10 others. There was not a single Indian to be seen as they carried off most of their dead. One unearthed grave, however, revealed the body of Chief Paugus, who was well known to the English.

Upon his return, Ensign Seth Wyman, who had distinguished himself in such an outstanding manner, was presented with a silver-hilted sword and made a captain. The General Assembly voted a sum of 1,500 pounds be paid the soldiers and their families in appreciation of their service. In addition, they offered a new inducement of four shillings per day be paid to volunteers and a bounty of 100 pounds per Indian scalp.

With this encouragement, a large company of men went north on a new venture, but had to turn back due to the extreme heat and sickness; many were sickened by the *bloody flux* and died, among them Captain White and Captain Wyman.

It took some time for the full impact of this fight to be analyzed. Historians wrote of Lovewell's victory, but at best the battle seems to have ended in a draw. But the remote, fierce tribe of Pigwacket Indians was dealt a severe blow. The surviving members of the tribe were led to the French mission village in Saint Francis by Chief Adeawando, who had survived the fight on the shores of Saco Pond. It would take a considerable amount of time before it would become a certainty that the Pigwacket tribe had actually abandoned their ancestral home.

On August 5 of the following year, the Indians signed a treaty marking the end of Dummer's War with the Eastern Abenakis.

In the following years, the fight at Lovewell Pond became the subject of ballads, poems and was the frequent topic of campfire discussions, with 1725 marking the end of Governor Dummer's War with the Eastern Abenaki. King George's War, of 1740 to 1748, however, was to follow, as was the Seven Year War, 1765-1763.

The following poem well depicts the famous fight:

LOVEWELL'S FIGHT
by Thomas C. Upham, 1824

What time the noble Lovewell came,
With fifty men from Dunstable,

The cruel Pequa'tt tribe to tame,
With arms and bloodshed terrible.

Then did the crimson streams that flowed,
Seem like the waters of the brook,
That brightly shine, that loudly dash,
Far down the cliffs of Agiochook.

With Lovewell brave, young Harwood came;
From wife and babes 'twas hard to part;
Young Harwood took her by the hand,
And bound the weeper to the heart.

Repress that tear, my Mary, dear,
Said Harwood to his loving wife,
It tries me hard to leave thee here,
And seek in woods the distant strife.

When gone my Mary, think of me,
And pray to God that I may be
Such as one ought that lives for thee;
And come at last in victory.

Thus left young Harwood babe and wife,
With accents wild she bade adieu;
It grieved those lovers much to part,
So fond and fair, so kind and true.

Seth Wyman, who in Woburn lived,
A marksman he, of courage true,
Shot the first Indian whom they saw,
Sheer through his heart the bullet flew.

The savage had been seeking game:
Two guns and eke a knife he bore;
And two black ducks were in his hand,
He shrieked and fell, to rise no more.

Anon, there eighty Indians rose,
Who hid themselves in ambush dread;
Their knives they shook, their guns they aimed,
The famous Paugus at their head.

Good heavens! They dance the Powwow dance,
What horrid yells the forest fill?
The grim bear crouches in his den,
The eagle seeks the distant hill.

What means this dance, this powwow dance?
Stern Wyman said; with wondrous art,
He crept full near, his rifle aimed,
And shot the leader through the heart.

John Lovewell, captain of the band,
His sword he waved, that glittered bright,
For the last time he cheered his men,
And led them onward to the fight.

Fight on, fight on, brave Lovewell said;
Fight on while heaven shall give you breath!
An Indian ball then pierced him through,
And Lovewell closed his eyes in death.

John Harwood died all bathed in blood,
When he had fought until set of day;
And many more we may not name
Fell in that bloody battle fray.

What news did come to Harwood's wife,
That he with Lovewell fought and died,
Far in the wilds had given his life
No more would in their home abide;

Such grief did seize upon her mind,
Such sorrow filled her faithful breast;
On earth, she ne'er found peace again,
But followed Harwood to his rest.

'Twas Paugus led the Pequa'tt tribe;--
As runs the fox would Paugus run;
As howls the wild wolf would he howl;
A large bear skin had Paugus on

But Chamberlain, of Dunstable,
(One whom a savage ne'er shall slay,)
Met Paugus by the water side,
And shot him dead upon that day.

The Chaplain's name was Jonathan Frye;
In Andover his father dwelt,
And oft with Lovewell's men he'd prayed,
Before the mortal wound he felt.

A man was he of comely form,
Polished and brave, well learnt and kind;
Old Harvard's learned wall he left;
Far into the wilds a grave to find.

Ah, now his blood red arm he lifts,
His closing lids he tries to raise;

And speak once more before he dies,
In supplication and in praise.

He prays kind heaven to great success,
Brave Lovewell's men to guide and bless,
And when they've shed their heart blood true,
To raise them all to happiness.

Come hither, Farwell, said young Frye,
You see that I'm about to die;
Now for the love I bear for you,
When cold in death my bones shall lie,--

Go thou and see my parents dear,
And tell them you stood by me here;
Console them when they cry, Alas!
And wipe away the fallen tear.

Lieutenant Farwell took his hand,
His arm around his neck he threw,
And said, brave Chaplain, I could wish
That heaven had made me die for you.

The Chaplain on kind Farwell's breast,
Bloody and languishing he fell;
Nor after this said more, but this,
I love thee, soldier, fare thee well.

Ah! Many a wife shall rend her hair,
And many a child cry, "Woe is me!"
When messengers the news shall bear,
Of Lovewell's dear bought victory.

With footsteps slow shall travelers go,

Where Lovewell's pond shines clear and bright,
And mark the place, where those are laid,
Who fell in Lovewell's bloody fight.

Old men will shake their heads and say,
Sad was the hour and terrible
When Lovewell brave 'gainst Paugus went,
With fifty men from Dunstable.

Though the Pigwacket Warriors left the field of battle first, it cannot be said there was a victor. Time and history have marked this event as a turning point in the settlers' long war with the Indians. The beautiful valley which is now the site of Fryeburg, Maine was the home of the Pigwacket Indians for thousands of years. Now, they were gone.[20]

There was one Pigwacket who still hoped to return. His valor and fighting skill were sorely needed at Saco Pond. The problem was that he had long been exiled from the tribe. As English and Pigwacket blood soaked the ground near his boyhood home by Saco Pond, he was on his small island at Big Island Pond in Derry, New Hampshire, preparing to move his adopted tribe to their summer camp at Great Bay. He would not learn the fate of his native tribe until spring of the following year.

---

[20] "Pigwacket,by George Hill Evans, 1939,(p.69) "Somewhere in the blue sheet of storied water that bears the name of Lovewell still holds in it's crystal depths the blue bowl of the sky, and the predatory Kingfisher still drops like a plummet from the out-thrust branches of the guardian pines. Somewhere in its golden sands lie peacefully together the moldering bones of red and white alike."

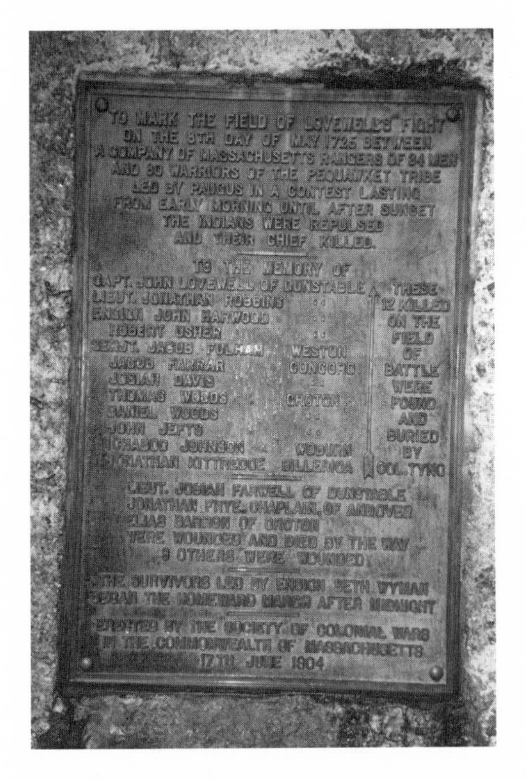

Top: Monument to Lovewell's Ranger. Bottom: View of Woods with Lake in background.

MONTIGNY AND ESCUMBUIT MEET AGAIN 1703-1706

The young Escumbuit's exploits in Newfoundland in 1696-7 and his revenge of Pascho Chubb's treachery in Andover marked the end of King Williams War, and was followed by five years of uneasy peace during which the border between the settlers and the Indians continued to be a no-man's land. The period beginning August 10, 1703 and ending July 13, 1713 saw a major renewal of the border war chronicled by Samuel Penhallow in his *History Of The Indian Wars*, published in 1726.

Penhallow was one of New Hampshire's best known officers, active in the Indian affairs of his time, and considered the main authority on the history of that period.

Francis Parkman, on the other hand, wrote the epic series of books entitled *France And England In North America*. From his days as a student at Harvard University until his death, he was a prolific writer on this subject. His books attempt to maintain a neutral tone between the two adversaries and their allies, whereas Penhallow was openly biased against both the French and the Indians.

The Reverend, P.F.X. de Charlevoix, S.J., was the author of *History And General Description Of New France*, written in French, in six volumes, translated into

English by John Gilmary Shea with notes. Like Penhallow, Charlevoix was openly biased in favor of the French and their Abenaki Indian allies.

The need to read up to six different writers' versions of the same event is important for several reasons. First, it tends to even out the bias of the various authors. Second, there were instances where only one of five or six accounts of the same incident mention Chief Escumbuit in connection with the event. Eventually, a pattern began to emerge to enable one to make accurate assumptions as to who took part in a campaign. For example, the daring Montigny is mentioned in connection with the 1696 capture of the English fort at Pemequid. Later in that same campaign, you find that his faithful Nescambiouit was with him in his attack on St. Johns.

The author neglected to mention that Nescambiouit was also with him earlier in this campaign when Chubb surrendered Pemequid. Now you can understand why Escumbuit, already incensed with Chubb's treachery under a flag of truce, vowed his vengeance after finding the Abenaki warrior almost dead from neglect, in the English dungeon. Another good example is the 1708 French and Indian raid on Haverhill described later in this story. Only *one* of the five accounts on this raid mentions that Chief Escumbuit distinguished himself in this raid by wielding the saber given him by Louis XIV in Paris, France, and that he received a musket ball wound to his foot. Omissions of this type explain why our information on Chief Escumbuit has been so sketchy and in some cases inaccurate.

The history of Queen Ann's war, covering the period from 1702-1713, is a litany of atrocities committed by the Indians. It soon becomes tiresome in its repetitious blood letting.

Some of the frontier towns of this period, in addition to the coastal settlements, were Kingston, Exeter, Hampton, Amesbury, Andover, Chelmsford, Groton, Haverhill, Deerfield, and Dunstable. There will be no attempt to describe every raid by two or three Indians in which a farmer was shot and scalped in the field, or a child taken captive and carried off to Canada. The first priority is on the Indian raids in which Escumbuit was involved. After that, selected stories have a unique slant or demonstrate the courage of the settlers and their ability to fight back.

Queen Ann's War, also known as the War Of The Spanish Succession, was declared in Europe May 14, 1702. When Governor Dudley was named to head the Colony in the same year, the Indians were described as being in a tolerable good frame and temper. Thereupon, on June 20, 1703, a Congress was appointed in Casco, Maine where the chiefs of several tribes met. Chiefs Mauxus and Hopewood represented the Norridgwalk tribe. Chiefs Wanungunt and Wanadugunbuent came from the Penobscot, Chief Wattanamunton from the Pennacook, and Adeawando and Hegen from the Pigwacket tribe. Also, the Chiefs Mesambomet and Wexar with about 250 braves in 65 canoes arrived in a festive mood.

They were well armed and all dressed in their finest buckskins replete with wampum decorations and colored face paint. Although mostly in a good mood, some displayed considerable arrogance. Strangely the important Sagamore, Escumbuit, was not present, for, he was given a key role in a secret plan to attack all the English gathered for the Congress.

A large tent was erected to accommodate Governor Dudley with the other English dignitaries and the Indian Sagamores. The Governor addressed the Indian chiefs in a conciliatory manner, saying, "I was commissioned by the Great and victorious Queen of England to come and meet with you, our friends and brethren to reconcile whatever differences happened since the last treaty." After a short pause, the Indian orator, Chief Simme, rose and delivered a speech of great eloquence and passion acknowledging the Governor's favor in giving them a visit with so many important people and assuring him that they aimed at nothing more than peace; that so high as the sun was upon the earth, so far distant should their designs be of making the least breach of peace between each other. With that, he presented Governor Dudley with a belt of wampum and invited him to the two pillars of stone erected at a former treaty. They then added a number of stones to this monument which they named *Two Brothers*.

This ceremony having been performed, several volleys of musket fire by both sides were exchanged and the Indians added their usual singing, dancing and loud exclamations of joy. Arrangements were then made to provide trading posts for the Indians with goods at favorable prices and a gun smith to repair their guns.

The Indian chiefs, Bomazeen and Samuel, then told the English that several French missionaries were among them recently asking them to take up arms against the English, but that they refused, saying, "They were as firm as the mountains, and should continue, so long as the sun and the moon endured."

French writers of this same period quote Father Sebastian Rale of Norridgewalk as saying the Indians told *him* that they had only signed a treaty of neutrality with the English, but that his Indians were ready to take up the hatchet against the English again. The historian Parkman suggests the Indians were merely telling both sides what they wanted to hear, hoping to get as much as they could from each side.

Two intrigues of the Indians failed during this council. When it came time to fire their muskets to celebrate the event, the Indians insisted that the white militia fire first. The English volley came from muskets not loaded with shot. The Indians fired next and it was discovered later that they had loaded their muskets with live shot with the intention of firing on the English, but were unable to do so since their chiefs were intermingled with the whites in the confines of the tent. (Penhallow, the historian present at the meeting, made this charge. However, one must not forget his bias against the Indians.)

The Indians asked the English to delay their departure until the Pigwacket Chief Watanummon arrived to join their council. After waiting several days, the English departed for Boston. Penhallow says that Watanummon was waiting for a combined force of 200 Canadians and Indians under Escumbuit's command to join him in a surprise attack on the English. Penhallow writes that they intended to capture the English and sacrifice them at their leisure. Chief Escumbuit, the important Pigwacket Sagamore, was not present at this meeting with the English. Had the Canadians arrived, Escumbuit, the most daring of the Abenaki chiefs, would have been given the role of wiping out the English Governor and his council.

On August 10, 1703, scarcely six weeks after the declarations of brotherhood and everlasting peace, 500 Indians, together with their French sponsors, struck from

Casco to Wells. This was the third onslaught on these settlements. Life in the outlying hamlets was exceedingly rough. For example, the house of Edmund Littlefield, reputedly the richest man in Wells, consisted of two bedrooms and a kitchen. This last was supplied with a table, a pewter pot, a frying pan and a skillet, but had no chairs, cups, saucers, knives, forks, or spoons. In each of the two bedrooms there was a bed, a blanket, and a chest. The people who continued to inhabit these border villages, at great danger to themselves and their families, were mostly rough, illiterate people willing to take a chance. The treaty signed at Casco six weeks earlier lulled the border dwellers into a state of complacency, prompting a great many people to return to these settlements, many of whom paid with their lives for their lack of caution.

On this day, the men at Wells were mostly at work in the fields which lay apart from the houses or out in the salt marshes. This town, which had stood its ground in two previous raids, suffered great damage with 39 persons killed or taken captive. Cape Porpoise, with only a few fishermen inhabitants, was overwhelmed and burned. The garrison at Winter Harbor defended itself well for a time, but eventually surrendered under terms.

Saco Fort was attacked and overwhelmed with 11 killed and 24 taken captive. The Jordan family of Spurwink lost 22 of their large family. The garrison at Scarborough made a vigorous defense.

The Indians sent in a captive, under a flag of truce, to induce them to surrender, but the commander of the fort retained the captive and defied the Indians. After a long siege, at the point of surrender, reinforcements arrived to save them.

Perpooduck was the home of nine families; they had no garrison to retire to and all their men were gone. Here the Indians butchered 25 and took 8 captives. The pregnant wife of Michael Webber was killed by a blow from an Indian war club and her stomach ripped open and part of her child cut out.

The most forward outpost was the fort at Casco Bay where 34 men were commanded by Major John March. He was unaware that the settlements south of him were under simultaneous attack by the Indians. When he saw a contingent of three Indians approaching the fort with a white flag, he decided to go out to meet them. These three Indians were the Sachems Escumbuit of the Pigwacket Tribe, Mauxus from Norridgewalk, and Wanungonet from the Penobscot. Prior to being sighted by the fort, other Indians had moved into concealed positions close by. The Major was accompanied by two old inhabitants of the place--a Mr. Phippeny and Mr. Kent. March's parting warning to the soldiers in the fort was, "Keep a sharp eye!"

As the three English approached, Escumbuit and the other two chiefs drew tomahawks from under their clothing and attacked March. He, being noted for his agility and strength, wrested a hatchet from Wanungonet and held Escumbuit and Mauxus at bay until Sergeant Hook and few soldiers came to his aid, managing to get the Major back to the fort. Wounded in the encounter, he managed to survive. But Mr. Phippeny and Mr. Kent, unable to defend themselves, were murdered where they stood.

The Indians soon appeared in force and began to burn all the cabins and property around the fort. After a few days, their numbers increased to about 500 Indians and a few Frenchmen under an officer named Beaubassin. They had completed their ravages down the coast and now proposed to take the fort on the shore of the bay where Escumbuit and his warriors managed to shelter themselves behind a steep bank which protected them from musket fire from the fort.

Here, they proceeded to dig their way towards the palisade under which they proposed to tunnel and launch a surprise night attack.

After three days, and very close to their objective, they suddenly came under cannon fire from the Province Galley commanded by Captain Southack. He had sailed into the harbor and captured three small vessels which had previously been taken by the Indians and he destroyed many of their canoes. Escumbuit and his Indians abandoned their siege. By daybreak the following day, they disappeared.

Thus began Queen Ann's War. The French Jesuit Historian, Charlevoix, wrote that "these raids, organized by the Canadian Governor Monsieur de Vaudreuil and led by the Sieur de Beaubassin, effected some ravages of no great significance; they killed, however, about 300 men."

He is incorrect on two counts: the dead did not exceed 160 and they were mostly women, children and old people.

Charlevoix adds: "The essential point is to commit the Abenakis so they can't turn back."

The French authorities did not relish a war on two fronts. Hence their policy on the frontier of New York was the opposite to their policy for New England. They left the former undisturbed because, by attacking the Dutch and English settlers, they could expect reprisals from the Five Indian Nations on that frontier. Their policy in New England was to keep the Abenaki tribes constantly stirred up to prevent these tribes from signing a permanent peace treaty with the settlers there. It was a policy which served them well for many years. There were Indians like Chief Madockawando, who knew they were being used by the French, but the more militant chiefs, influenced by the Jesuits, would not listen to him.

On February 8, 1704, Joseph Bradley's garrison home in Haverhill was taken in a surprise attack. Indians scouting the garrison entered when they saw the gate open and no sentry posted. A pregnant woman of the house was boiling soap. When they burst in on her, she dumped the large pot of boiling lye over one of the Indians, scalding him to death. They killed the sentry, who was supposed to be guarding the entrance and took several captives including the pregnant woman--the second time she had been held captive by the Indians. Half starved and forced to carry a heavy load, somehow she managed to keep up with her captors in their retreat to Canada. In the course of the march, they allowed her to bear her child in the middle of the wilderness. However, the child so annoyed the Indians with its constant crying for food, they killed it by pouring hot coals from their fire down its throat. To her dismay, this remarkable woman managed to survive the long winter march to Canada where she was sold to a Frenchman, who eventually redeemed her to her husband.

Early in 1704, 50 Canadians and 200 Abenaki Indians were sent against the New England border, under the command of Hertel de Rouville, who, with four of his brothers, led the large party within two miles of Deerfield, Massachusetts. On February 28, 1704, they lay half starved and frozen outside the palisade which enclosed a settlement containing a wooden meeting house and 11 private homes with their sheds and barns.

Outside the palisade, on the road to Hadley and Hatfield, lay another 41 houses. The attacking force laid low all day in a pine forest, half famished and cold, fearing to light the fires which might reveal their presence.

There had been ample warnings of an attack and, for some time, all of the townspeople were sleeping inside the palisade for protection. Now that the panic subsided, the people moved back to their homes. There were 268 inhabitants and 20 yeomen volunteers in the town as a whole. A fierce winter storm had recently deposited a good three feet of snow covering the meadows and the frozen river and there were wind-driven drifts much deeper than that.

Two hours before dawn, de Rouville and his men, leaving their snow shoes and packs behind, were able to crawl over the crusted snow drifts which had reached the top of the eight foot palisade and dropped into the compound of the silent, unwary village. With screeches and war whoops, they assaulted the doors of the houses with axes and hatchets. A young man named Stoddard, sleeping in an upper room, managed to snatch a cloak and throw himself out the window after which he made his way half naked and frozen to Hatfield.

In the ensuing melee, 53 settlers were killed and 111 prisoners carried away. Historical records show those escaping death or captivity at 137. Rouville organized and drove the prisoners north while some of his men stayed behind still trying to invade those houses which resisted.

A man named Wells, who lived at the south end of the village, gathered about 50 men and attacked and killed several of the stragglers, driving them out of the town and across the crusted snow. Wells was unable to control some of these young men who discarded their jackets in their eagerness to pursue the stragglers. Meanwhile, Rouville, hearing the firing, turned back to set an ambush in which nine of the undisciplined youngsters were killed and one of their number captured.

The attack and rape of the settlement of Deerfield and the fate of the 111 taken north is an epic of suffering and courage. It was well chronicled by the Reverend Williams, minister of Deerfield.

Two of his seven children, too young to make the march, were killed in his house. About three days on the march north, his wife was dispatched with a single tomahawk blow because she was unable to keep up. Later on, the party split into smaller groups and he was separated from his children. On reaching Canada, his children were placed in convent schools where they were under constant pressure to convert their religion.

Reverend Williams was well treated by the French and entertained by various members of the Catholic church. In spite of his efforts, he was unable to be reunited with his daughter. The low point of his experience came when he received the news that one of his sons had converted to Catholicism. He was later returned in a prisoners' exchange.

The death of loved ones at the hands of the marauding Indians was as devastating to family and friends as could be imagined; yet there was a finality that, in the end, had to be accepted. Those who were carried off as captives left behind many mixed emotions beyond the normal feelings of grief. In most cases, those carried off were women and young people into their early teens.

The men were normally killed during the raids, and the fate of Hannah Duston's baby at the hands of the Indians shows that the Indians often considered it too much trouble to carry a baby or very young children all the way to Canada to be ransomed to the French. Having been taught by many Puritan preachers that the Indians were Godless savages without redeeming features, you can imagine the horror in the minds of parents whose children were carried off by the Indians.

If the captives survived the long trip to Canada, they were normally sold to Frenchmen. A number of women stayed with their Indian captives; in some cases, they even married Indians. One woman in western Massachusetts stayed with her Indian husband in spite of the entreaties of her family to return. She bore her Indian husband two children and she and the children visited her former home every year. Each year her family would beg her to give up her Indian life and stay with them, and each year she chose to return to her husband and her tribe.

Young girls were generally placed in convent schools where they were able to note the missionary zeal of the nuns and priests with whom they came in contact. They were well cared for in a family atmosphere, and in many instances embraced the religious atmosphere with its processions, gold crosses, incense and rituals. All this seemed more meaningful to the young captives compared to the severe rituals of the Puritan church.

During the course of the border wars, 1,600 men, women and children were carried off by the Indians. Many were later ransomed and returned to their families. A large number of young girls became nuns and stayed in Canada. Many women married Frenchmen and were absorbed into the society of Quebec and Montreal. Many found life in these cities more exciting than their life in the rude colonial settlements. In general, they did not encounter the treatment they had imagined in the hands of the Indians, who did not sexually molest them during captivity. One theory is that Indian ritual demanded that the brave deny himself sex while on the war path. More logical is the explanation that the captor realized that his captive might end up an adopted member of his own tribe and felt obliged to treat his captive with respect.

As in all generalities there were exceptions to the rule. Many a woman was killed by a blow from a war club or tomahawk, then scalped, her body left by the side of the trail when she was unable to keep up with her fleeing captors. Some of these exceptions are included in this story. It is obvious that some of the historians of the period began their story with a premise, after which they proceeded to include only those facts which supported their particular prejudice. The Indians did not treat all their captives well.

After the failure of his plan to ambush the English Council at Casco, and his unsuccessful attack six weeks later on it's garrison, Chief Escumbuit received no historical mention in the lesser actions that followed.

After the coordinated attack by the combined Indian/French forces desolated the frontier from Wells to Casco, the pattern of the war became a series of hit and run raids upon targets of opportunity. Chief Escumbuit continued to cut notches in his war-club during 1704 and 1705 as he ranged the frontier in smaller hit and run raids. As stated previously, the raids are so numerous and so repetitive, in the misery they created, that it serves no purpose to detail each and every one of them.[21] Escumbuit, we shall shortly see, needed no urging by his French allies to join a fight. Indeed, his appetite for mayhem would become too strong even for their taste.

Turning our attention to Newfoundland, (where the failure of the French to occupy St. Johns and the other English settlements they had captured in late 1696), was coming back to haunt them. These Newfoundland settlements were of strategic importance to the English. The

---

[21] History Of The Indian Wars, Samuel Penhallow, 1727: As to the treatment of our captives with the French, it was as different and various as their tempers and constitutions, while others were morose and sordid; but the Indians might as well alter their complexions as their constitutions; for scarce a day past without some act of cruelty, insomuch that all were under a constant martyrdom between fear of life and terror of death. It would be an endless task to enumerate the various sufferings that many groaned under, by long marching with heavy burden, through heat and cold; and when ready to faint for want of food they were frequently knoct on the head: Teeming women, in cold blood, have been ript open; others fastnd to stakes, and burnt alive; and yet the finger of God did eminently appear in several instances of which I shall mention a few. As first of Rebekah Taylor, who after her return from captivity, gave me the following account. That when she was going to Canada, on the back of Mount Real River she was violently insulted by Sampson, her bloody master, who without any provocation was resolved to hang her; and for want of a rope, made use of his girdle (rawhide belt), which when he had fastned it about her neck, attempted to hoist her up on the limb of a tree, (that hung in the nature of a gibbet) but in hoisting her, the weight of her body broke it asunder; which so exasperated the cruel tyrant, that he made a second attempt, resolving that if he fail'd in that, to knock her on the head: But before he had to effect it, Bomazeen came along, who seeing the tragedy on foot, prevented the fatal stroke. (Sampson and Bomazeen are two Indians frequently mentioned in historical accounts of the time.)

offshore waters offered vast schools of cod which were essential to the commerce of the New Englanders. If the French held all of Newfoundland, the fishing fleets of the colonists would be at great peril. For this reason the tug of war for Newfoundland went on from 1696 to 1705, when the English rebuilt their fort in St. Johns.

D'Subercase proposed to the court of Louis XIV that he take the King's ship, *Wesp*, to Canada. With these orders, he sailed to Quebec, where he took on 100 Canadians, landing them at Placentia, the main French settlement on Newfoundland. Among this group were 12 officers, one of whom was the famous Montigny. These Canadians joined de Subercase, who set out on January 15, 1706 at the head of 450 well armed men. Among them were soldiers, Canadian civilians, privateers and Indians led by Escumbuit.[22]

Montigny and Escumbuit were delighted to be reunited and Montigny took the Indians under his command at

---

[22] History Of The Indian Wars, Samuel Penhallow, 1727 (p 30). "The Descent that the enemy made on Newfoundland was more terrible and surprising than the former; for on January 21,[st] 1707, at break of day, Monsieur Supercase, Governor of Placentia, came with five hundred and fifty French from Canada; who ransacked and a company of savages, of whom Assacumbuit was Chief and laid waste all the Southern settlements in a few days and then fell on St. John, where in the space of two hours all were become prisoners of war, excepting those in the castle and the fort. The night before the enterprise they were obliged to lye on a bed of snow, six foot deep, for fear of being discovered, which caused such cold and numbness in the joynts of several, that Assacumbuit vow'd revenge, and accordingly executed his resentment, for that he destroyed all before him, and gave no quarter for some time; till Monsieur de Beaucourt, who was a gentleman of more humanity, did interpose and abate his fury.

once. Each man carried provisions for 20 days, his arms, a blanket and a tent for each mess. When one considers the far north location of Newfoundland, one has to wonder what motivated these men to undertake a two week march through snow and arctic temperatures and to cross three rivers, not yet frozen, in order to attack an enemy stationed in heated forts with adequate provisions.

On reaching St. Johns, they lay overnight in deep snow in icy cold conditions. To avoid detection by the local inhabitants, Escumbuit denied his warriors the comfort of fires to keep them warm. At daybreak, they fell upon the houses outside of the fort. Escumbuit, incensed by the dreadful conditions they had to endure during the night, ran amok for some time, giving no quarter until he was finally restrained by Monsieur de Beaucourt, the French commander. They took 140 prisoners whom they sent into the fort, not out of pity, but to deplete the food supply of the garrison.

They laid siege for 30 days, but the fort, under the command of Captain Moody and the Castle commanded by Captain Lotbarn, rejected all threats to surrender.[23]

---

[23] History Of New France, The Rev P. F. X. De Charlevoix, S.J. (p.174) "On the 5th of March the army decamped and marched along the shore to Ferryland, where the inhabitants at first made a show of defense, but they soon changed their minds and surrendered as prisoners of war. That town was burned, after which Montigny, who had brought his faithful Nescambiouit on this expedition, was detached with the Indians and a part of the Canadians to go in the direction of Carbonniere and Bonavista, with orders to burn and destroy all the coast, which he executed without losing a single man, so great was the terror among the English. His very name made the arms fall from the hands of the most resolute, and gave him a number of prisoners whom he had only the trouble of binding. But he had to reserve Carbonniere Island for another time. It held three hundred men, and was, as I have

The other communities in the area, however, were destroyed by Montigny and Escumbuit.

The campaign concluded in the spring after which the Canadians were transported back to Quebec on the *Wesp*, while Escumbuit and his warriors went down the coast on a French sloop to Penobscot Bay from where they returned to their village.

In parting, Montigny told Chief Escumbuit that when he needed him again he would get a message to him through Father Thury's mission. Escumbuit and his braves were loaded down with civilian loot from the St. Johns attack; in addition, they were given extra blankets, gunpowder, musket balls and tobacco.

Before parting, they were also served with wine and brandy; but the French wisely refrained from giving them the custody of spirits for the trip home. They gave the captain of the ship some kegs of wine with the admonition to keep it under lock and key, and the captain scrupulously doled out a ration of wine to the Indians before each evening meal.

When Chief Escumbuit and his warriors got back to their home in the White Mountains, the tribe was already preparing for the trip down the river to their summer camp in the area of Saco and Biddeford. They were received with the customary celebration especially when the

---

stated, inaccessible in winter. Every other place was carried or submitted; Messrs. De Linctot, de Villedonne and de Beletre, thoroughly supported Montigny, and Nescambiouit, as usual, distinguished himself. In time, this campaign completely ruined the English trade in Newfoundland."

tribe learned that they had lost only 3 of the 41 braves gone to Newfoundland with the French.

The women of the tribe had been complaining for some time about the loss of their young braves in the never ending war against the English. It affected their lives in many ways. The men were needed to bring back the annual kill of moose, deer, and bear. In their absence, the winter had been very hard on these families. The storage caches of smoked meat empty, many had subsisted on the fish they had caught through holes chopped in the ice of the river and the lake.

They were used to hardship, no matter its cause, so their complaints went muted as the men danced their *scalp dance*. Escumbuit's own wife displayed the correct enthusiasm over the blankets and the metal cooking pot he had brought back, but her mind was fixed on getting something substantial to cook in the pot.

Their marriage evolved into a kind of arrangement. As they had no children, Escumbuit suspected that his wife had acquired bad demons which prevented her from bearing him a son. He was away more than any of the men of the tribe, always restless, always angry and filled with hate for the white man. It never occurred to him that his wife might have eyes for another man, for, was he not Chief Escumbuit with merit beyond the thoughts of his fellow braves?

His wife's family was very large, her lineage that of an important Pigwacket Chief and her family was important in the village. Although the Indians had no written language, they were wonderful genealogists. The Indian family was based on a patrilineal system. An important Indian could recite his lineage through the male members of his family for many generations. In certain rare cases, a family would be matrilineal after an outstanding woman ancestor, but this was rare. Within a tribe, only persons of different family lineage were allowed to marry.

Escumbuit became indifferent to his wife, especially because she was no longer the slim, fleet, young thing he had married. Furthermore, he discovered that the important things he had done and discussed with his French allies were of little interest to her. In short, they had grown apart mainly due to his restless energy and drive to be in the limelight he had craved since his lonely youth. His wife's younger brothers had both taken brides in the village and one of the brothers and his wife shared the same wigwam with Escumbuit.

The brother-in-law was named Wejack for the ground hog. For some time, he used his family connection to attempt to learn the whereabouts of Escumbuit's silver mine. His logic was solid enough:

"You are the husband of my sister. Thus you are my brother. Your friend Moosu is dead and now you have no one to help you dig and carry the lead. It is only just that I take his place to help you to share the mine with our family."

Escumbuit listened disdainfully to this line of reasoning more than once and it always ended the same:

"My Manatou, the eagle, revealed the mine to me. When my Manatou tells me to share the mine with you--so shall it be. Until that time, it is my secret."

Now Wejack, cowed by Escumbuit, was reduced to complaining to his sister outside of the Chief's hearing.

Studying the lithe young body of Wejack's bride, Escumbuit began to think:

"Wejack, you speak like a squaw. When it comes time to step forward to fight the English you disappear like the turtle beneath the water. How does a squaw like you merit such a woman. Would that she were mine."

The practice of polygamy did exist to some extent among the Indians, but this was one of the things the Jesuits worked hard to stamp out. They sermonized constantly against drinking rum or whisky and against conjugal infidelity. Perhaps the reason they worked so hard on these two things was the tendency for one to beget the other.

Escumbuit found a unique way to solve his families' food shortage. He began to take trips to his mine alone, and a day's work at the mine loading a splint basket mounted on his back-pack provided him enough metal to mold, not only musket balls, but sinkers to be used on fishing lines. He traded these necessary items with other Indians for whatever dried meat they could spare to fill his own birch bark storage box.

In June, they rolled up the bark covering of their wigwams and loaded their worldly goods into their canoes for the leisurely paddle downstream to the coast. On reaching their traditional summer camp, the men went out in search of tall, thin saplings to cut and bring back to camp. The two inch butts of the poles would be buried about two feet into the ground in a circle. Then the slender tips would be bent and lashed together with the cordage made from the inner bark of the bass-wood tree to form a rounded frame. The men and women rolled out the birch and elm bark shingles to cover the structure, leaving openings for an entrance and a smoke hole in the peak. Then all they had to do was cover the floor with their rush mats and build a low pallet around the perimeter for a sleeping platform. This was their summer home until the break in August, when they went up river to pick corn.

This was a marvelous time of the year for the Indians. Just as modern people flock to the seashore anticipating a break from the rigors of the winter, the Indians were no less eager for their annual migration. The spectacle of hundreds of canoes filled with braves, squaws and children, all in their colorful costumes, paddling down stream to the ocean was a sight to behold.

The women decorated their faces with red and black pigments and used shading around their eyes to enhance their beauty. The men, even more colorful, added white, and ochre and displayed the standard two feathers of the Abenaki brave in their top notch.

Many of the canoes were decorated with intricate designs painted on the white birch bark sheathing and often the family totems were carefully painted on the bow of the canoe. The canoes themselves were things of fragile beauty. The Indian canoe tended towards a higher upsweep to the bow which gave the craft a classic look.

But the spirit of the people was most impressive. The children laughed and shouted across the water to their friends. The squaws smiled and chattered and even the braves got into the spirit, shouting good-natured jests back and forth between the canoes. Everyone looked forward to the fresh oysters and clams, the lobsters and quahogs and the flesh of the seal and porpoise roasting over an outdoor fire.

Food was so plentiful that the braves could indulge themselves in games like lacrosse which they played on the beaches. They sat around in informal groups, smoking their pipes and talking male talk, while the women had their own groups to gossip and discuss food and cooking recipes.

The arrival of a white trader in his boat full of things the Indians craved was the next anticipated event. All of the families had furs to trade for goods and the men looked forward to buying small bottles of the white man's rum. In spite of the admonitions of Father Bosquette in his daily sermons, there was no way to keep the braves away from rum if it were available.

Even their village Jesuit looked forward to his summer at the seashore; in many ways it made his work easier. On arrival, he set up a small crude chapel made out of a few poles covered with bark and most of the Indians came by daily to pray at this chapel. Since everyone had more time for leisure, they were more relaxed and more receptive to his sermons.

Father Bosquette was not a militant Jesuit like Sebastian Rale at Norridgewalk or Father Thule on the Kennebec. The Canadian authorities gave up trying to use him as their political tool to stir up his Indians against the English. The fact was that by nature, the Pigwackets were more savage than many of the other New England tribes. The Quebec officials finally realized they could handle this tribe without his help and they allowed him to concentrate on saving souls.

When the trader finally came early in June, the Father was one of the first to go out to his ship because there were a few small things he wanted to buy. He bought his needs with French livres, a currency equivalent to an English shilling. The trader accepted all negotiable currencies as well as furs in exchange for his goods.

Captain Turner accepted him aboard cordially and violating his own advice to his Indians, he accepted a cup of rum from the Captain.

"Father", the Captain then said, "I've a packet for you from the Friar at Placentia that I've been carrying with me for the past month. Let me give it to you now before we get down to our trading."

With that, he went below to his cabin. On returning, he handed him a small sealed package. Then he went to talk to some of the Indians to allow the Friar to open his package in private.

On opening it, he withdrew a letter which he began to scan quickly. Suddenly, his mouth opened in an involuntary gasp of surprise. He read further with a look of incredibility on his face and finally put the letter back in the package, thrusting it inside his robe where it lay supported by the cord around his waist. Later, after buying his cooking utensils and needles and thread, he left the ship.

"You know our Chief Escumbuit well," he said to the Captain. "When he completes his trading, please tell him that I have an important message for him."

With that, he paddled back to shore and returned to his wigwam where he immediately went to work mending his robe with his new needles and thread.

When Escumbuit came aboard with Atchitemon, he took care of his own needs first. He bartered some of his musket balls and fishing sinkers for his personal supply of rum after which he traded for some cooking pots and metal spoons that his wife needed. Then Captain Turner, in his passable Algonquin, related the message:

"Chief, I brought a message to the Friar from Newfoundland and he told me he has some important news for you. Do me a favor and don't drink that rum until after you have gone to see him. He will be very angry with me if he knows I traded rum to you."

The Chief nodded his agreement and went ashore with his wife and their purchases. True to his word, after beaching his canoe, he sent his squaw to their wigwam with the trade goods and headed for the Friar's chapel.

Father Bosquette set aside his mending when he saw Escumbuit and gestured for him to sit on the ground near him, offering his bag of tobacco. After they lit up, he reached inside his robe and pulled out the letter. Looking directly into Escumbuit's eyes, he spoke in good Algonquin:

"Chief, this letter bears a message of great importance to you. It comes from across the great lake which lays before us and it comes from the ruler of all the great chiefs of my country. You have heard me speak of his Majesty Louis XIV, King of France. He has heard of your great service to his kingdom and he requires your presence in the palace of Versailles to honor you. He also desires to honor your commander, Sieur de Montigny, at the same time. You are to travel to the Kennebec by the first of August. From there Father Thule's Indians will take you to Castin by canoe where you will find His Majesty's man-of-war, the *Wesp*, which is sailing for France the middle of August. Montigny will meet you there."

In spite of the momentous news, Escumbuit remained outwardly impassive while his mind reeled with its meaning. His thought had been that the French were calling him for a new campaign in the north or perhaps to inform him of the loss of a comrade-at-arms, but this was so unexpected. He needed some time. Father Bosquette, recognizing this, continued:

"You will have many questions and I will have many instructions for you. Go now and tell your family and the tribe. We can talk later. But, first, kneel with me and pray to him who has divined that this wondrous thing should happen."

Chief Escumbuit drank too much rum that night after telling the news to the braves gathered around his campfire. It was a reaction that should be understood and excused by a thoughtful person. How often does history arrange for a Stone Age Indian to travel through a time warp of 3,000 years to the lavish stage of Versailles and an audience with His Majesty, King Louis XIV of France?

Wigwam

Top: Garrison House, Wells, Maine. Bottom: Monument to Defenders of Garrison.

CHIEF ESCUMBUIT IN FRANCE 1706-1707

In the weeks following the arrival of the letter, Father Bosquette spent a great deal of time with *his* convert, preparing him for the culture shock awaiting him in France. Native born and educated by the French Jesuits, he knew that, to some degree, Chief Escumbuit's conduct in France would be a reflection on himself and his work with the Indians.

There was separate instruction in the letter for the Chief to wear his native costume. The writer also noted that the King was particularly interested in seeing his famous war club and his beaver fur cloak decorated with British scalps.

A separate letter held an ornate card which stated that the bearer was a guest of the King of France and that he was to be given whatever services he required without charge. Any charges for travel, accommodations and food were to be noted on a bill to which the Chief would affix his totem acknowledging that he received these services. The provider of these services would then present this bill to the King's ministry of finance in Paris for payment.

The Father also coached him in such basic things as the use of indoor toilet facilities and the importance of maintaining his personal cleanliness. He also showed the need to modify his Indian eating habits. It was considered good form in Indian circles to eat noisily and express frequent grunts and exclamations of pleasure over the cook's preparation of the food. The Jesuit knew that it was futile to try to extract a promise from the Chief that he would not drink on the trip. Instead, he implied that the strong brandy of the French might eat a hole in his stomach, cautioning him to drink only the wine.

Meanwhile, Atchitamon and her sister-in-laws were busy sewing new clothing for Escumbuit. They traveled to the coast bearing all their worldly possessions, including a number of beautifully tanned deerskin hides, and selected three of the most luxurious to make new shirts. One was an almost white creamy hide and the other two were a beige color and a dark brown. The coloring was determined by the length of time the hide was smoke cured in the final operation. They also made two new pairs of leggings, several breech clothes, and two new pairs of moosehide moccasins. The final decorations were painstaking work, but were considered essential details for clothing designed to be worn in important ceremonies.

For centuries the Indians used the inner surface of the common quahog shell to make wampum, having devised a way of cutting the lustrous pearl like material into small uniform pieces which they drilled and strung into beautiful belts. The wampum was used as currency and was often proffered as a good will gesture at treaty signings. They used the same method to decorate their deerskin clothing which they wore in Indian ceremonies of all types. They also sewed on cut sections of porcupine quills which were colored with natural plant dyes. They were skillful craftsmen as existing artifacts attest.

By this time however, the traders learned that the Indians preferred the colored glass beads which were manufactured in England and shipped to America to be traded in exchange for furs. Also, the natural fibers formerly used to string the beads and porcupine quills had been replaced by strong English twine.

When the time approached for the Sachem's departure, the tribe organized a huge celebration during which there was much feasting, dancing and singing by all the members of the tribe. The Chief's Council met and each Chief and Sachem had an opportunity to make his solemn, dignified presentation to the assembly. This Indian custom has been noted in several historical accounts. In many ways, the Indians seemed undisciplined, but in their own council meetings and their treaty discussions with the English, they followed a very structured form. Some of them were formidable orators and when they came forward in their solemn way to speak, they were never interrupted by their fellow chiefs.

Finally, the Chief was off, buoyed by the well wishes of the tribe and accompanied by five braves, who accompanied him as far as the Kennebec. There, some of Father Thury's braves took him up to Castin by canoe. When he reached Castin's trading post, he learned that a small French sloop in the bay was headed for Placentia, the French port in Newfoundland, where he would find the *Wesp* and her two accompanying sloops. Five days after boarding this French man-of-war, they hauled anchor and sailed for France.

The Sieur De Montigny was aboard when Chief Escumbuit arrived, and was more excited by this adventure than the Chief himself. Montigny, a Canadian, was a noted fighter; but, unlike most of the ship's officers, he was not a member of the elite.

He was younger than Chief Escumbuit; in spite of his common background, he had the élan that one might expect of a French officer. He was not quite as tall as Escumbuit's six feet, but with his athletic build, his fair hair and a complexion darkened by constant exposure to the elements, he was an impressive man. His outgoing personality contrasted to the Sachem's quiet demeanor, but together, they presented a formidable pair.

The two shared a cabin in the officers quarters and ate with the ship's officers. Montigny was amused by the Chief's discomfiture with his cabin bunk, but after stiffening the padding with underlying planks, the Chief was satisfied.

Chief Escumbuit was on several raids in which he and his men were carried in French sloops commanded by D'Iberville. He was accustomed to the motion of the ship and was not affected by sea sickness. The constant confinement, however, wore on him. Montigny filled much of his time helping him improve his French. In the end, it remained little more than a French patois, understandable, but certainly not polished.

Escumbuit had a lot of time to observe and compare and he particularly noted how the French officers held absolute authority over the common sailors of the crew. An Indian chief led by example, and the braves followed his example acknowledging that he was a better fighter. From what he could see, it was not the same with the French officers. Many of them appeared physically weak and some of them almost effeminate in their manner. He began to realize the sailors were responding to the uniform and not always to the man inside the uniform. Escumbuit, though an uneducated man and out of his natural environment, was not stupid. With his native shrewdness and a cunning, matching the animal predators of his homeland, he could survive anyplace.

The Chief enjoyed walking the deck of the ship and inspecting the large number of cannons the ship carried. On the lower gun deck he walked with a stoop because the headroom was too low for his large frame. The French sailors and their officers viewed this formidable man with awe. His demeanor was not threatening in any way, but as one of the French officers commented to Montigny, "The savage has a menacing way about him that chills the blood."

Montigny laughed and responded, "That is why we have him fighting on our side."

The crossing was made without incident. As they neared the English channel, the captain sent the two fast sloops ahead to scout the channel for English war ships. The winds were favorable. When the sloops reported no enemy sightings, the captain decided to make the run up the channel to LeHavre. As the *Wesp* sailed up the channel on a port tack on a clear bracing September day, the high spirit of the crew was contagious as the ship neared its home port.

After dropping anchor in LeHavre, many of the ship's officers together with Montigny and Escumbuit transferred to a smaller sailing vessel for the trip up the Seine to Rouen. Paris lay some 240 miles inland on the Seine River; it would be several days before the party would arrive there.

In Rouen, they transferred to horse drawn carriages. The ship's officers, however, insisted that they continue on as a party and eat and sleep in the same inns and restaurants. Because the Chief and Montigny attracted so much attention in the port of LeHavre and in Rouen, the naval officers wanted to arrive in Paris as part of their entourage. In the age-old manner of sailors home from the sea, there was a lot of wine and brandy poured and they were all in high spirit.

The Sachem was becoming used to new and different scenes as the days passed. When they got to Paris, the sheer size and majesty of the buildings and the press of the throngs walking the streets astounded the old Chief. Nothing he was told prepared him for what he now saw and experienced.

Their friends took them to the appropriate government departments to be assigned royal housing. Their passes cut through the bureaucracy and they were treated with deference by the officials who attended them. The naval officers advised them to bypass Versailles on route to Paris so as to avoid being assigned quarters near the palace. They correctly guessed that these two would be much more comfortable living in the bustle of the city within walking distance of the garish flesh pots of Paris. From here it would be a mere carriage ride to the palace at Versailles when summoned for their audience with the King.

Pressing their local addresses on Montigny, the French naval officers urged him to look them up when he and his colorful companion were in a mood to enjoy the sights and sounds of Paris.

Louis XIV reigned as King of France longer than any other French monarch. When his Italian-born Minister, Cardinal Mazarin, died in 1661, the King surprised everyone by refusing to replace him, electing instead to assume his duties. During his reign, he attempted to dominate Europe by military force. Known as the *Sun King*, together with his wife, he sponsored the greatest cultural revolution of France, responsible for razing the medieval protective walls around Paris and replacing them with broad boulevards like the famous Champs Elysees. He founded academies of painting, sculpture and science and he built *Invalides*, the home for war veterans. He also refurbished the famous cathedral of Notre Dame. This hands-on King was a working monarch, who regularly met with his council on Monday, Wednesday and Saturday to discuss problems of the state.

Unlike the English, who mostly complained about the expense of supporting their colony in New England, the French King tried to micro-manage the war between his Canadian outposts and the New England colonies. Nevertheless, Louis XIV was never able to resolve the tensions between his governing élite committed to efficiency, and a society organized by rank, birth and privilege.

These tensions would finally reach their climax in the French Revolution of 1789-1799 in which the great grandson of Louis XIV would be beheaded.

King Louis XIV was responsible for four wars, the last being the *War of the Spanish Succession* known in New England as *Queen Ann's War*, terminated by the Treaty of Utrecht in which the King ceded Indian territory in Maine and New Hampshire to the English.

The Abenaki Indians signed this treaty without realizing they were signing away ownership of their ancestral lands. The King and his ministers were looking at lines on maps showing territories 3,000 miles away about which they knew very little.

Construction of his palace at Versailles began in 1661 and Louis and his court moved there in 1682. This magnificent structure remains the showplace of Europe. The western facade of 1900 feet long (longer than six football fields) faces a large open area in which the statues of famous Frenchmen are displayed. There are gardens with secluded groves and a grand canal one mile in length. Spectacular fountains are supplied with water from a system originating 100 miles away. The palace itself features numerous salons, galleries and royal apartments--all lavish in their design and their appointments. Its most outstanding feature is the Hall Of Mirrors where the Germans had the French put their signatures to their surrender in World War II.

Nothing could be more bizarre than plucking an Aboriginal Indian from the desolate wilds of central Maine and inserting him into what was the acknowledged showplace of the civilized world. Until they were contacted by French and English traders about 1640, the Abenaki knew neither weapons, nor tools fashioned from metal, nor clothing woven from the fiber of domestic animals.

The Chief lived pretty much as his ancestors had done for over ten thousand years before him. With his code to live by, he was friendly to people who met him as a friend, but was an implacable enemy to those who did him harm. He had a simple concept of right and wrong and did not seem to suffer from guilt. He believed there was an after life, but his understanding of higher beings included spirits both good and evil. He believed in appeasing the evil spirits, but accepted the bounty of the good ones. When it came time to die, he died with dignity, with the knowledge that he was moving on to another life. He had no guilt for the atrocities he committed on his enemies for they would have done the same to him.

The Indian was born, lived and died in a very simple society. It is understandable why the apologists for the Indians say that we cannot condemn them for living by the rules of their own closed society.

The calendar of the court of King Louis XIV was very full. It was not surprising that it took a full two weeks after their arrival that Montigny and Escumbuit were given a date for their audience with the King. In the meantime, the two cut a swath in Paris society.

Montigny dragged Escumbuit to some of the cultural centers of Paris, but he had no interest in art museums or string quartets. They spent a lot of time frequenting the café society and were often joined by various naval officers they had befriended on the *Wesp*. In short, Montigny and Escumbuit became the toast of the town.

Montigny bought an outfit of local clothes for his companion, and soon learned that the people wanted to see *Le Sauvage* in his own native costume. In fact, the owners of some of the establishments pleaded with Montigny that he too wear his fringed buckskins when he brought Escumbuit to their place of entertainment. They also reminded Montigny to be sure to have the Indian bring his war club. In fact, the locals loved to hold and count the notches of the club, with hardly a thought given to the corrolation between those notches and the caved-in human skulls they represented.

The women of the Paris night-life were absolutely taken by the sight of *Le Sauvage*. attaching themselves to him like Velcro, no matter that they did not carry any kind of conversation with him. Just to be seen with him was sufficient.

Montigny watched over his companion very carefully. On a few occasions, after imbibing a quantity of wine or brandy, the old Chief tended to draw into himself, that when pressed by admirers, his eyes flashed a signal prompting Montigny to intervene to prevent a disturbance.

Although Escumbuit allowed people to handle his war-club, he demanded that it always to be within arms reach. However, he always carried his knife thrust into the waist cord which supported his breech cloth.

A date was set for them to appear for their audience with the King at the Palace of Versailles. The King's representative visited their apartment and asked if they were comfortable and if they had any requests. He then carefully detailed how and when they were to appear, explaining how they were to conduct themselves in the King's presence. He said the King had expressly requested the Chief should appear dressed in his native costume, including his famous cloak, that he should bring his war-club and apply his war paint decorations.

Since Chief Escumbuit planned on appearing before the King exactly as described, this request did not present a problem. If the King had requested him to appear in French clothing, *this* might have caused difficulties. First, he was proud of his Indian culture and second, he had noted the effect of his clothing on the French populace.

On the day of their appearance, word spread that this was the day in which *Le Sauvage* was going to appear before the King, resulting in the court's overflow with men and women of the French nobility. One of the many Courtiers remarked, "It is almost what one would expect if His Majesty were going to receive a foreign monarch."

Montigny and Escumbuit were ushered into a setting which was lavish beyond description. Nervous, Montigny noted with some surprise that his companion seemed to be completely serene, as if he were merely keeping an appointment with destiny.

Montigny was honored first by being knighted and having his rank raised to a Colonel in the French Colonial Army. After receiving his sword, he stepped back to make way for Chief Escumbuit.

The attention of the assembled was riveted on the tall figure of Chief Escumbuit, striding to the dais on which the King stood. A full head taller than the average man in the room, Escumbuit stood silently with great dignity, awaiting the King's words. From the two feathers in his scalp lock to the wampum decorated moccasins on his feet, he was dressed as an Abenaki Warrior, his face painted with the white, black and red markings of a brave on the war path, designed to strike terror in the heart of his enemies. His fine soft deerskin shirt was decorated with intricate patterns of colored beads. Above his moose hide moccasins, he wore deerskin leggings held up by cords suspended from the rawhide girdle holding his deerskin breechcloth in place. His head was shaven, except for the scalp lock at its back which held the two feathers of an Abenaki Warrior. The tawny color of his arms and face were marred only by the light colored scars of his numerous battle scars. On his shoulders rested his beaver skin cloak, adorned with a gruesome assortment of human scalps. In his right hand, he carried his famous war-club.

There was a long moment of silence in the great hall when the Courtier gestured for him to make his speech to the King. As the large assemblage listened intently to hear every word, Chief Escumbuit raised his war-club over his head and began to speak in his slow untutored French:

"Your Imperial Majesty! So long as the sun shall rise on the People Of The Dawn shall the Abenaki warriors fight at the side of the French against the English. This hand of mine has slain one hundred and fifty of Your Majesties' enemies within the territory of New France. So long as the English come, so shall the French soldier and the Abenaki warrior dance the "scalp dance" over their dead bodies."

The King, hearing and understanding the words, clapped his hands with delight, whereupon the crowd burst into a thunderous applause.

The King descended from his throne. Advancing towards the Chief, King Louis XIV gestured for an assistant to pass him the beautifully crafted sabre which featured a silver hand guard. On cue, Escumbuit kneeled as the King rested the tip of the blade on the Chief's shoulder.

"Chief Nescambiouit of the territory of Arcadia in New France. As King of France, with this sword, I declare you to be a knight in my service. With this honor, I declare that the treasury of France shall pay you the sum of eight livres each day for the remainder of your life... Vive La France!"

This being the finale of the day's events, the crowd applauded long and loud and the ladies pushed their husbands forward to approach *Le Sauvage*, hoping to feel the danger radiated by his person. Montigny, also the center of attention, came to the Chief's rescue in order to field the many questions and invitations offered to them. Escumbuit stood silent, letting Montigny speak for him since he scarcely understood a word of what was being said.

An assistant to a Jesuit priest approached, introducing Montigny to his superior. He was the Reverend P.F.X. de

Charlevoix. Montigny quickly recognized him as the important Jesuit who had been in Canada several times.

Charlevoix exchanged a few comments then asked if it would be possible for Montigny and Escumbuit to visit him at the Cathedral of Notre Dame the following week for an interview. Montigny knew that the Jesuit was an historian. Sensing it might be important to himself and to Escumbuit, he readily accepted the invitation. Pleased, Charlevoix stepped back, a smile on his face.

The honored guests were then taken on a tour of the palace which took up the remainder of the afternoon. One of the King's council told them, on leaving, that their presence was requested at a costume ball given by the King the following week, again His Majesty requesting that they be dressed accordingly.

They arrived at Notre Dame Cathedral the following week at the appointed time. Construction on the Cathedral began in 1163 and was completed in 1250. They stood for a moment, gaping at the famous flying buttresses--an architectural marvel, which support the high vaulted ceiling inside the cathedral without the use of interior columns. The cathedral was in a state of excellent repair, having been recently refurbished by order of the King. Escumbuit must have been impressed by its size if not its beauty, for certainly he had never seen anything like it among his people.

They were ushered into a study where Charlevoix greeted them, serving each a glass of wine. He then explained that he was a historian and that his life work was to record the history of New France, the name he had given to that part of the new continent. He was working on the fifth volume of his history, covering the period from 1696 to the present.

He surprised them with his knowledge of their campaigns in Newfoundland and questioned them about some of the details not quite clear in his mind, telling them he was aware of their reputations as fighters, assuring them of the right of their cause, adding that almighty God was on their side.[24]

Escumbuit must have realized that besides God, the Europeans had much more on their side; they had industries, transportation, and huge populations on the move. He saw the plentiful horses, and must have heard of the mechanical horses yet to come--sobering thoughts for his subconscious.

Charlevoix took his leave of the pair after touring the cathedral with them and after having shown them the renown *rose windows* still famous today. He did not neglect his duty as their priest and advisor and left them with a warning to beware of the temptations and the debauchery of the city. They thanked him and took their carriage back to their small apartment in the city where they prepared for another night on the town.

---

[24] "Handbook Of American Indians North Of Mexico, by Frederick Webb Hodge: He confirms that Assacumbuit met Charlevoix in France. Escumbuit is listed under his Indian name Assacumbuit and the author mentions that he was also known by the French as Nescambiouit and by the English as "Old Escumbuit".

Author's note: The work of Charlevoix was finally completed in six volumes, and was translated to English by John Gilmary Shea. His description of Montigny and his "faithful Nescambiouit" and the terror they inspire in the English gives the impression that they were favorites of his; as indeed they were.

King Louis XIV was a stickler for detail, having issued orders that Chief Escumbuit be given instruction in the proper use of his new sabre. The Monarch was not told that fully two thirds of Escumbuit's victims were women, small children and old people. The writings of Charlevoix consistently plays down the nature of the attacks and who the actual victims were. Probably the King had some romantic notion of his noble savage fighting hand-to-hand in a classic duel. In any case, Montigny and Escumbuit reported to a nearby military academy where they were to receive instructions from a master swordsman.

The art of swordsmanship is a complicated business. In modern fencing there is competition in three weapons. The foil is a slender straight weapon with a sharp point designed to puncture the vital organs of the opponent. It has no cutting edge and the area in which points can be scored extend from the groin line to the neck line. In modern fencing matches, the tips of the foil are protected with a rubber button and the face of the swordsman is protected by a mesh covered mask.

The epée is heavier, without a cutting edge, and points may be scored on the arms and legs as well as the body.

In a sabre match, you have both a pointed end which can puncture and a sharpened curved blade for slashing. Mounted cavalry men used the sabre as an effective weapon to thrust to a vital spot, or inflict a disabling wound by slashing an opponent's arms, shoulder or legs.

The demonstration given by the fencing master and another Frenchman was impressive in its violence and its grace. Thrust and parry--Slash to the neck and a high parry--slash to thigh and low parry. So it went--back and forth, like a pair of karate combatants delivering blows and counter blows that look violent, but hurt no one.

The instructor, handing Escumbuit a practice sabre with a dull blade, asked him to get up. In slow motion, he took him through the technique of using his blade to parry the thrust of his opponents to allow the tip to pass harmlessly by his body, in slow motion how to parry a high slash to the neck with a high parry either left or right. Then he continued with the method of parrying a slash to the legs by turning the tip of the sabre down to counter the blade of the opponent, and so on. It looked somewhat like a ballerina giving dance lessons to a truck driver.

But, as Escumbuit got the knack of it, the action began to quicken. The fencing master was a bit of a dandy and couldn't resist making the Chief look awkward and a little silly. Suddenly, with the Chief's eyes narrowing, he rushed his opponent delivering a high slash to the neck which the instructor attempted to parry. The force of Escumbuit's charge carried him right through the attempted parry, knocking the fencing master flat on his back, as the Chief stood over him with the point of the sabre pressed to his instructor's throat.

In that awkward moment, Montigny leaped up and moved forward to put his arm around the Chief's shoulders, drawing him off the dueling floor.

There was some uneasy laughter on the part of the spectators a bit horrified at the Indian's lack of style in his savage rush at his opponent. He obviously had not followed the rules of the dueling match. But it was not lost on the spectators; they witnessed, probably for the first time, the instinctual actions of a natural born killer. Recommending that the lessons be ended for the day, they all went off to a local café for wine and lunch. The tension subsided and they had a good time.

Escumbuit was in Paris for about seven months and the whole sense of his relationship with the white man was turned upside down. Now, his long held beliefs were being challenged. As a result, he was confused and troubled. From his earliest contact with the white man he lived with a chip on his shoulder. Faced with the fact of the white man's superior technology--his metal tools, huge cannons, sailing ships and even his fine woven clothes, he was forced to admit they were far more advanced than any of his people.

He rationalized the differences by ridiculing the white men as poor woodsmen and hunters, looking down on them for being farmers where only squaws worked the fields in Indian society. He condemned the white man for failing to protect his family from Indian attacks. In short, he developed a full blown inferiority complex.

Up to now, he had been hiding his resentment and feeding his ego by showing his superior courage, his fighting skill, and his ruthlessness. He deliberately projected this image to his own people as well as to the French and English. Like a high school bully, he discovered the role which brought him the attention he craved.

He had plenty of reason to hate the English, and his relationship with the French was little better than lukewarm. While he sought their praise for his fighting skill, he remained aloof.

This visit to France forced him to revise some of his beliefs. He expected to see little more than larger versions of the English frontier settlements he successfully devastated back home. He was not prepared to see such splendors as the Palace of Versailles and the Cathedral of Notre Dame. He was also unprepared for the hospitality and the open admiration of the élite, who clamored for his company.

He was like famous entertainers or athletes beginning to believe the write-ups. He was vaguely aware of the masses of poor people in the city. As he became comfortable in the company of the nobility and of the élite, he began to adopt their attitude towards the lower classes. It was these elitist attitudes, coming out of a class system, that sowed the seeds of hate and envy which led to the French Revolution at the close of the century.

Gradually, the Chief was being seduced into the comfortable feeling that he was a superior being, that the world was finally accepting him as an embodiment of his Indian name:

"Chief Assacumbuit, he who is so important and raised so high by his merit, that thoughts cannot reach his greatness." He was unprepared for the rude awakening awaiting him on his return.

The months flew by. As the winter faded into spring, the two heroes become an accepted part of the Paris scene. Escumbuit gradually learned to accept Montigny as a friend and his ability to communicate in French improved noticeably.

One spring afternoon, they sat sipping wine at a table in a side-walk bar. Dressed in French clothes, Escumbuit afforded them an anonymity which they welcomed. Turning to Montigny, Escumbuit began to speak:

"I do not understand why the French and the English are at war in my country. Here, the French have everything a people could want. They are rich and powerful and the English live far away in another land. Why must they fight the English?"

Montigny explained that the French and the English had warred with each other for centuries. Escumbuit interrupted:

"Look at this great city. The French have many cities almost as great as this. Why do they not send all their soldiers in one great raid to the land of the English and kill them all and take their women and children captive? Then the French and my people could rule the English in Boston, and we could live in peace in the land of my ancestors."

Montigny smiled at the Chief's inability to grasp the reality of the situation. Placing his hand on the forearm of his friend, Montigny continued:

"But, Chief, the English are even more powerful than the French. They have many large war ships and their city of London is as great as Paris. Neither nation has the power to defeat the other. I agree that the French should stay in their country and the English on their island. In North America, we Canadians have all the land we need in the north. If the English would go no further north than Massachusetts, the Indians would be left in peace and we Canadians would be happy. The problem is that the English want to steal the Indians' homeland and drive them all to Canada. If we let them do this, then, they will want Canada as well."

The Chief nodded his head as if he understood. Then, he lapsed into a troubled silence. Montigny looked at him.

"Chief, why do you fight the English with so much hatred? So far they have not burned your Pigwacket villages or killed your women and children. Do you fight because you are a warrior and it gives you pleasure to take the English scalps as you would a bear for his fur, or is there another reason?"

The Chief thought for a moment. "When I was a boy, my tribe ruled a valley where the white man never came. We killed animals for our food with the bow and arrow. We made our clothes from the skins of these animals and we lived well in our village by the lake. We grew our corn and our tobacco there. In the summer, we went to the seacoast and our Indian spirits were good to us there. We ate the oysters and clams and killed the water fowl which came in great numbers. We did not have all the things that the white man had, but we were happy. We did not weep over the things we did not possess or know about. Then the English came. At first we were his friends. Then they cheated us of our lands. When we gave them land, it was never enough; they always wanted more. That is why I hate the English and why I will fight them to my death."

Montigny was surprised at the complexity and depth of the Chief's thinking. He deftly moved to close the subject: "Well, now that I understand how you feel, I think it's time we go to the naval headquarters and find out when we can make passage on a ship to take us back home. It looks like we are both ready."

On visiting the naval office, the lieutenant in charge told them that the *Heros*, a two masted sloop, was leaving the next month and that if they would check him in a week, he would tell them if the ship's captain could give them passage. In a few days, they received a message telling them that the captain was in the city and that he had invited them to travel with him to Le Havre on May 5.

They now began their final round of invitations and farewell parties given in their honor. With a departure date set, they counted the days, feeling no regret at having to leave. Suffering from homesickness to some degree, and each in his way, they were anxious to get back to tell their friends of the wonderful things experienced in France.

The Jesuit Charlevoix sent letters for each to deliver to fellow Jesuits in Maine and Canada. Finally, on May 5, they headed for LeHavre by carriage with Lieutenant Oulette, captain of the sloop, *Heros*. On May 12, 1707, the sloop sailed with two other sloops bound for New France. Escumbuit and Montigny stood silently at the stern for a long time watching the coast of France fade from view, each immersed in his own thoughts.

FALL OF CHIEF ESCUMBUIT 1707-1708

When the *Heros* entered the harbor of Placentia, the moment arrived that Chief Escumbuit had hoped would never come. He and Montigny were going in different directions: Montigny would stay with the ship until it reached Quebec, and Escumbuit would be heading south to join his tribe in Maine.

Except for his boyhood friend, Moosu, who had been killed during the raid on Salmon Falls, the Chief had never allowed anyone to penetrate the wall he kept about himself. His relationship with his wife and her family was little more than an arrangement since he never learned to confide his private thoughts to his wife.

Montigny had a breezy, open way about him that quickly endeared him to almost anyone he met. His most outstanding characteristic was that he was completely unprejudiced. Minorities have a fifth sense about prejudice, and Escumbuit's instincts had signaled him that Montigny's open acceptance of him was genuine. Montigny succeeded in breaking through his reserve, but now, they were splitting up. Like most men, they managed to effect the separation with little sentiment.

Montigny swore that they would fight together again and that was good enough for Escumbuit. They stared into each other's eyes for a brief moment, shook hands and went their separate way.

Montigny was sent to fight the English and their Iroquois allies in the west where he and other French officers were forced to surrender to the English and the Iroquois Indians. In negotiating terms for their surrender, Montigny and his companions begged they not be turned over to the Indians.

The Iroquois were the most cruel of all of the Indian tribes. It is interesting how fate turned the tables on Montigny, who had fought so many battles with Indian allies at his side.

By the time Escumbuit made his way south to the Pigwacket summer camp in the Biddeford area, it was late June. Now, like the fictional time traveler, he was traveling backward through time to a culture thousands of years older than the one he had just left. Would he be able to make that transition without problems?

He was welcomed home enthusiastically by the members of his tribe, anxious to hear about his experiences in France. They marveled at the lethal beauty of his silver handled sabre and the fine cloth jacket he brought back with him.

The Indians held their traditional festival in which the tribe feasted, danced and sang, while the Chief's Council met to question their famous Chief about his trip.

Although no promises were made when Escumbuit left the previous summer, many in the tribe expected the Chief to come back with some sort of news which would effect their own life for the better. When they learned that all the news involved the Chief and the honors which had been heaped on him by the King, they soon tired of hearing about the details of his trip and his great successes in

Paris. Mostly they anticipated his homecoming to see how he would react when told about the great, good fortune of the tribe--the good fortune that *he* had brought them.

They were unable to trace the origin of the story, but somehow the mystery of the silver in the Indian musket balls had been traced back to those molded by their own Sachem--Escumbuit. The Indians knew the value of silver, having heard how the settlers hoarded silver in the form of coins, eating utensils and jewelry. The news that the metal used to make musket balls came from their own region was interesting. When they learned that this same metal also contained silver, excitement reigned. Although they knew that Escumbuit held the secret to the mine's location, the question of the day became: Is not this mine the property of all the Pigwackets?

The Chief's Council discussed the issue of the silver mine several times during Escumbuit's absence, deciding to feel the Chief out individually rather than confront him immediately upon his return, hoping he would conclude on his own that the entire tribe should benefit from his find. In the meantime, the chiefs merely reported the discovery to him at one of their Council meetings.

Escumbuit listened carefully with no outward sign of emotion. Finally, he said something to the effect that he would have to check to see if the report was true. The assembled chiefs had to settle for that response for the time being.

When the Chief left Paris, he was given his accumulated pension in the form of a small purse of gold he carried in a deerskin pouch hung from his neck. He was told that his pension would be paid at the same time Father Bosquette received his salary from the Canadian authorities. Like the Jesuit, Escumbuit would have to exchange his gold coins and French livres for trade goods such as tobacco, steel sewing needles, hatchets, blankets, fish hooks, and glass beads--to be exchanged for the Indian staples such as maize, meat, vegetables, shell fish and animal skins.

It gradually became apparent to the tribe that the Chief not only had a secret silver mine, but he apparently had an income from the French authorities. He and his family did very little hunting and fishing. They exchanged tobacco and other trade goods for their daily needs and they lived very well with very little work.

If one had to describe the politics of the Indians, one certainly wouldn't describe them as capitalists, concluding that if anything, they were socialists. Certainly the way they lived had a great leveling effect. It was predictable that Chief Escumbuit's new found prosperity would become a source of envy and discontent. By the time they moved back up the Saco River to their village in the White Mountains, in late September, the dissent in the tribe was barely contained. Only two things kept a lid on the simmering pot: first, their Sachem was a highly dangerous and unpredictable man; secondly, he had steadfastly refused to make any comment which would reveal his intentions.

Escumbuit's year long absence from his family did not improve the atmosphere at home, either. Atchitamon turned out to be a rather unkempt Indian squaw and the Chief found her dull compared to the stylish women in France. The Indian lifestyle, which he formerly idealized as superior to that of the white man, now seemed squalid by comparison. He became demanding of others and impatient with their response, having become used to being served by those he considered his inferiors. He was incapable of diagnosing the reason for his discontent. As a result he became morose and withdrawn.

Confused and depressed, he decided to take a trip up the Saco to bring back some ore from his mine. He packed food for five days and loaded his canoe with his back-pack mounted splint basket and a metal shovel he intended to use at the mine. Telling Atchitamon he would return in five days, he pushed his canoe into the stream and paddled north. Late the first day, as he angled the canoe for the shoreline to stop for the night, he spotted a canoe far behind him. He pulled the canoe well up on the shore and turned it over to provide some shelter when he slept that night. He kept a vigil at the shore for some time, curious to see who was in the other canoe. When darkness came, he assumed the people behind also landed to camp for the night and dismissed them from his mind.

The following day, he headed up river again. After rounding a bend, to a position which blocked his view to the rear, he paddled to shore and beached his canoe. Running quickly down the shore, he reached a spot where he could look back down river without being seen. Although the canoe was more than a half a mile away, its silhouette showed there were two occupants. He ran back to his own canoe and continued up stream. He now knew the trailing canoe was following him. With two people paddling, they would have caught up and passed him some time ago.

He reached his silver mine about noon, but continued to paddle past that point for another hour. He beached his canoe so that the stern protruded slightly from the bushes, to be sure it would be noticed by the sharp eyes of his trackers, and moved through the brush leaving signs any good Indian tracker could follow. Choosing a thick hemlock, its dense branches brushing the ground, he planned his ambush. Retracing his path by a different route, he positioned himself to see if they would spot his canoe and land. In about 20 minutes, the canoe with its two occupants headed for the shore directly toward his canoe. When they closed the distance to about 200 yards, Escumbuit recognized the two braves: his brother-in-law Wejack, and the younger brother of Chief Adeawando.

Escumbuit quickly returned to his ambush hidden by the dense hemlock boughs. As he waited there, he felt consumed by a burning rage.

The two Indians in the trailing canoe had indeed followed him. They were so far back that when the canoe ahead disappeared from sight around a bend in the river, they continued to paddle expecting to regain sight of it. Following at a great distance, they thought they had not yet been seen by Escumbuit.

It was Matasqua, brother of Adeawando, who talked Wejack into following Escumbuit to learn the location of the silver mine. At first, Wejack was afraid, but when his friend told him that they did not have to confront Escumbuit, he agreed to the plan. Once they learned the location of the mine, they then could tell the members of the Chief's Council and let them use the information to confront Escumbuit, adding that Escumbuit would never know of that he was betrayed by his own brother-in-law.

Rounding the bend of the river and failing to see Escumbuit's canoe ahead, they knew he must have landed someplace. Inspecting the bank on both sides of the river, they continued to paddle until Wejack saw it.

"There it is on the left bank. Land above that spot and we can walk back and track him from where his canoe lays."

They carefully back tracked to the canoe. "His basket and shovel are gone", Wejack noted. "Let us track him, but we must be very careful. Once we find the location of the mine, we will mark this spot and return to the village."

With Wejack leading, the pair moved upward through the dense forest following Escumbuit's trail. Leaving their muskets in their canoe, each carried a hatchet and a dagger.

Chief Escumbuit, kneeling in his hemlock hiding place, already decided what he must do. Feeling nothing but disdain for the two braves following him, he showed little regard for the fighting ability of Metasqua and even less for Wejack. He waited silently, his senses tuned to a high pitch, like a tiger stalking its prey. They approached his position--Wejack in the lead--head down, following the faint trail, with Metasqua three paces behind. When they passed no more than two yards from his hiding place, Escumbuit struck.

Rising silently, he stepped up behind Metasqua, encircling his neck with his powerful left arm. In the same motion, he reached around in front. With an upward ripping motion, he buried his dagger under the rib cage directly into his heart.

Wejack whirled just in time to see Metasqua drop at the Chief's feet. Finding himself facing his brother-in-law with the bloody dagger in his right hand, Wejack, thinking he was about to die, raised his tomahawk, and began to charge, swinging the blade at the Chief's head. Dodging to the left, Escumbuit rammed the blade upward into Wejack's side where it deflected off his rib cage and leaving him a wound that exited from his back. Feeling the searing pain in his side, Wejack suddenly bolted in panic, his appetite for the fight gone. He was young and agile and began to run faster then he had run in his life.

Escumbuit followed for a few yards. Then, realizing the futility of catching Wejack, he returned to the dead body of Metasqua, picked up his hatchet and knife, and returned to his canoe. Having tied Wejack's canoe to the stern of his own, he started down stream, leaving Wejack to die alone in the woods.

He abandoned any thought of working his mine. The next day, he cast the spare canoe adrift downstream with the current. If someone were to find it and identify it as belonging to Metasqua or Wejack, it would not be difficult to conclude that the two drowned in the river.

Arriving at the village, he resumed his routine with no comment neither on his trip nor on the fact that he was back empty handed. Atchitamon's family knew Wejack went off with Metasqua, but it would be several days before they began to wonder when he was coming back. He had told no one about his conspiracy with Metasqua to learn the secret of Escumbuit's silver mine.

On the fifth day, Wejack returned to the village, weak and hungry, the deep wound under his right arm very conspicuous.

Escumbuit resigned to the fact that Wejack might make his way back to the village, but his outrage at the betrayal of his brother-in-law and his friend was not lessened by any guilt over what he did. He acted according to his Indian code: he was wronged and those who betrayed him had to pay. Also, he felt no need to explain the circumstances to anyone in the tribe. He dealt with the problem, and, as far as he was concerned, the issue was closed. However, he was to find that it would not be so cut and dried to Atchitamon, to her family, or to Chief Adeawando, the older brother of Metasqua.

By the time the Chief's Council met to discuss the murder of Metasqua and the stabbing of Wejack, sentiment against Chief Escumbuit was running high. The honors heaped on him by the French, especially the pension, combined with his knowledge of the silver mine, had created jealousy in the tribe. His arrogant attitude and, now, his murder and wounding of two members of the tribe eliminated any possibility of support from within the tribe. Not even a member of his wife's family stood before the Council on his behalf for the obvious:

"We must remember that Chief Escumbuit has been our bravest warrior. We cannot forget his trip to France, the knighthood by the King, his silver sword, the pension of French coins--he earned these things by his merit. The silver mine he hides from us was shown to him by his Manatou. Those who followed him to learn the secret of his mine meant to steal what was his alone. We must consider all these things before we judge him."

That type of defense over his actions was never made, not even by Chief Escumbuit himself. Wejack told the Council that he was only trying to learn the secret of the mine for the good of the tribe, that he and Metasqua expected no personal gain. In the end the council bowed to the temper of the tribe and to the anger of Chief Adeawando, the father of the murdered brave. They voted to strip Escumbuit of his titles as chief and as Sachem and to banish him from the tribe. There would be no immediate confrontation between him and Chief Adeawando's family. This was not the Indian way. They would wait their opportunity to revenge the death of Metasqua and strike when Escumbuit least expected it to happen!

The Chief went to his deserted Wigwam, quickly gathered his possessions, which he tied to his back pack, and left immediately. No one of the village spoke to him as he strode out of camp heading south to Ossipee. The silver handled sabre swinging from his side in its ornate scabbard was the only thing that set him apart from any other Indian as he made his way south.

He had thought about his situation and was now executing a pre-planned course of action. He decided against going to the French missionary village at Saint Francis in Canada. Many of the Pigwacket tribe moved up there and soon the details of his disgrace and banishment would be known there. Therefore, he headed for the small band of displaced Indians living on the big island at the lake close to the English. This would be the last place Adeawando and his relatives would be looking for him in order to take their revenge.

He was sure to be welcomed there and that if he arrived before December, he could offer to join them for their winter hunt.

He felt a sense of relief at his change of fortune. For some time, he thought of leaving his wife. After the attempted murder of her brother, it would have been impossible to live with her family. As to the rest of his crimes, as seen by the council, he did not feel one shred of guilt.

In his own mind, he still felt completely justified in his actions. The mercurial nature of his people that changed them from admirers to enemies almost overnight, sounded a warning to him. He must be more careful in the future about revealing the details of his income and information about his possessions to others.

He strode into the camp of his adopted tribe in late November in 1707 to begin a new phase of life. He did not intend for this to be his permanent home at the time. In a vague sort of way, he was hoping to be reunited with Montigny and possibly become a permanent part of his future.

The small band of Indians on the island was happy to see the old Chief once again. Each remembered him from his last stay when he and his small band went down to Andover and killed Chubb and his wife. They also heard the stories of his exploits since, and were honored to have him as a guest in their camp. He told them only what was absolutely necessary to explain why he wanted to stay with them for the winter.

Their band was short of able bodied braves and he was welcomed without reservation. He was invited to stay in the wigwam of an old brave and his wife, who welcomed the addition of an active brave to assist in the constant search for food.

Escumbuit was now past his prime by Indian standards. The average Abenaki had a life span of about 45; but there were individuals who lived into their eighties as well as children who died before the age of two. So, the average age was misleading.

At 42, Escumbuit was still strong and active and wasn't even thinking about getting old. Like most men, he had plans of great things for himself.

With the coming of winter, snow covered northern New England, marking the hunting season for the Indians. Outfitted with snow shoes, and pulling toboggans carrying food and bark to cover their temporary shelters, they went north for deer, moose and bear.

The deer and moose were taken more easily when their ability to run was hampered by the deep snow. Bears, on the other hand, were usually smoked out of their hibernating dens and easily killed in their befuddled state.

Escumbuit enjoyed the hunt, the hardships of living and hunting in the snow; and, dragging back the meat-laden toboggans was good for him. Thoughts of his adventures in France came less frequently now, and it was good to be an ordinary Indian once again.

The old couple with whom he lived on the island had a widowed daughter named, Metaxta, whose husband was killed during an Indian raid against the settlers, and now lived with her daughter Ramona, married to Hinkum. They had a daughter named Bluebird.

Metaxta was younger than Escumbuit, but she was still attractive. It was natural that her continuing contact with her parents brought her in contact with Escumbuit.

The rules of courtship and marriage which applied to a 14-year-old girl did not apply when it came to a widowed woman looking for a protector. It was natural that in time Escumbuit and she would build their own wigwam into which they would move their possessions and form a family unit.

Escumbuit found his new wife, Metaxta, appealing, and he was pleased to have a new daughter as well, albeit that of another man. On the surface, at least, Escumbuit seemed to have quickly rehabilitated his sagging fortunes. When winter came, they moved into the tribal longhouse which provided better protection against the cold and where the multiple cooking fires kept the temperature above freezing, where they survived the winter, cooking, eating, sleeping and telling stories.

The large raiding parties of the French and Indians gave way to smaller bands that continued to harass the entire frontier between the settlers and the Indians.[25] This isolated band of Indians, displaced by the advancing settlers, went unmolested mainly because they refused to join in the raids against the English. Hindsight should have told them they were living on borrowed time. But it would be another 56 years before the final peace treaty with the Indians would be signed.

Unknown to the English in early 1708, there were big plans afoot in Canada. Governor Vaudreuil called a great

---

[25] "History Of The Indian Wars" by Samuel Penhallow, (p.40): "The charge of the war was by this time so great, that every Indian we had kill'd or taken, cost the country at least a thousand pounds. But while they continued in great bodies, they did not commit the like spoil and rapine(in proportion) as they did before. August the 10th they slew William Pearl of Dover, and a little after took Nathanael Tibbits. But of the Indians that was ever known since King Phillip, never any appear'd so cruel and inhumane as Assacambuit, that insulting monster, who by the encouragement of the French went over to Paris, and being introduced to the King, lifted up his hand and in the most arrogant manner imaginable, saying "This hand of mine has slain one hundred and fifty of your Majesty's enemies, within the Territories of New England & C. Which bold and impudent speech was so pleasing to that Bloody Monarch, that he forthwith Knighted him, and order'd eight Livres a day to be paid him during life; which so exalted the wretch (having his hands so long imbrued in innocent blood) as at his return, to exert a sovereignty over the rest of his brethren, by murdering one and stabing another, which so exasperated those of their relations, that they sought revenge, and would instantly have executed it, but that he fled his country, and never return'd after."

council in Montreal, which included the chiefs of all the Christian Indians settled in the colony. These and other Abenakis were to join with 100 Canadians and other volunteers making up a force of 400 men. Messieurs de St. Ours des Chaillons and Hertel de Rouville were to command the French and the Sieur Boucher de la Perriere was to lead the Indians. The plan was for them to split up into several smaller parties which were to make their way to the south end of Lake Winnipesaukee by separate routes so as to not attract attention. At this rendevouz, they would be joined by many other Abenaki Indians including those from the Pigwacket tribe. From there they planned to descend on the Pistcataqua settlements of Berwick, Salmon Falls, Dover, Portsmouth, Oyster River, Durham and others. But when the French reached the rendezvouz, near what is now known as Wolfboro, the Pigwacket Indians and other Abenakis failed to show up, causing them to scale back their plans. Instead of a general attack on the previously mentioned settlements, they turned their attention to the town of Haverhill on the Merrimac River. Despite all the secrecy, word got to Governor Dudley in Boston that something was afoot, ordering that the settlements be reinforced with militia men. Outlying roads were also being patrolled.

The same rumors also reached Chief Escumbuit, now living on the main island at Big Island Pond in southern New Hampshire. In May, he went up to Concord to the Penacook Indian Village, whose Chief promised Escumbuit that he would let him know if and when the large raiding force was to come through the area.

Although the small number of braves in his adopted tribe had declared neutrality, Escumbuit had no intention of missing this raid. For one thing, he was out of action too long; more importantly, he felt there was a good chance his friend Montigny might be leading the raid.

On August 24, 1708, a messenger arrived with the news that the raiders were headed for Haverhill. A couple of days later, he joined the raiding party in Hampstead. By Saturday night, the French and Indian raiders lay in the woods on the heights above the village of Haverhill.[26]

Early Sunday morning of August 29, 1708 the people of the small village were sleeping in, planning to go to church and spend the rest of the day at leisure. The village still consisted of no more than 30 houses grouped down by the river with a few more scattered here and there. Up on the crest of the hill, a garrison house, owned by Jonathan Emerson, guarded the approach from Little River, with another one flanking it in the opposite direction. Three or four soldiers were recently posted to each of the various garrison houses because of the perceived threat. Beyond the garrison house, on the crest of the hill, stood a virgin forest which the settlers avoided.

---

[26] History Of New France by Charlevboix (p.206): "Our braves were not dismayed on learning that the enemy were so well prepared to receive them, and no longer trusting to a surprise, resolved to make it up in valor. They rested quietly all that night and the next day, one hour after sunrise, drew up in battle array. Rouville made a short address to the French to exhort all who had any quarrels with each other to be reconciled sincerely, and embrace, as they all did. They then prayed and marched against the fort. Here they met with a vigorous resistance; but at last entered sword and ax in hand, and set it on fire."

The constant raids by small Indian bands, killing and taking prisoners, kept the residents close to home with the river at their back for protection.

This day the French, painted like their savage allies, infiltrated via the banks of the Little River by-passing the outlying garrison houses. A lone settler, who happened to be up at that early hour, spotted the assailants filing silently out of the woods. Shouting an alarm, he fired his musket as he ran for the protection of a garrison house. It was too late!

Whooping and yelling, the invaders descended upon the houses of the town in a maelstrom of destruction and terror. The inhabitants, still in their beds, were awakened by the hellish sounds and made desperate attempts to save themselves.

One woman burst from her house running for her life to reach a nearby garrison. A bullet was quicker, making her the first victim of the assault. Houses were easily taken, others stoutly defended. Benjamin Rolfe, minister of Haverhill, ran to his door to make sure it was locked. The assailants fired through the door wounding him; then, bursting through the shattered door, they murdered him, tomahawked his wife, and smashed their infant on the door step killing it instantly. Two soldiers posted in the house begged for mercy, but were slain. A Negro woman named Hager took two other children down to the cellar, hiding each them under large wash tubs. She then hid behind a large barrel of meat in the corner of the cellar. The marauders quickly searched the cellar, helping themselves to the meat from the barrel behind which Hager crouched, trembling with fear. Only the darkness of the cellar and the haste of the assailants saved the woman and children.

Another woman named Anna Whittaker, a resident of the same house, saved herself by hiding behind an apple chest kept under the stairs.

The French, painted like savages, acted worse than those they imitated. In the house-to-house assault, they were equal to the Indians in their savagery. At the house of the Hartshornes, Thomas and his three sons were killed as they tried to escape. His wife pushed her children through a trap door in the floor before she joined them, closing the door over her head, leaving her baby on a bed in the room for fear its cries would reveal her hiding place. The savages entered the room. On seeing the helpless child, they tossed it out the window where it landed on soft ground, miraculously surviving the fall. The trap door escaped discovery, and fortunately, the house was not burned.

In another incident, a man named Swan tried to bar his door against the enemy. Unable to do it, he set his back to the door calling for his wife to help keep the invaders out. The Indians managed to force the door partly open at which point his wife picked up a meat spit. With both hands and the full weight of her body, she drove it through the opening, impaling the Indian on the other side of the door, thus saving their house and their lives.

The burning and pillage went on unchecked until the attackers heard a drum roll and a trumpet signaling the approach of the militia from the outlying garrisons. After putting the meeting house on fire, they began to retreat with their captives and all the plunder they could carry.

The fire in the meeting house was extinguished and the survivors mounted a force of men to pursue and attack the French and Indians. This force of 60 0r 70 men caught up to the retreating force and pressed their attack. The invaders were forced to drop their plunder and meet the attack of their pursuers. There was a fierce engagement in which they left 9 dead on the ground. Due to their superior force, they managed to drive the settlers back and resume their retreat carrying their prisoners with them. However, they had to abandon most of their plunder and their packs; worse than that, two of their French officers, Chambly and Vercherer, were killed in this skirmish. In all, the French admitted to having 18 of their men wounded during the day. French accounts[27] added that "the monster Assacumbuit performed prodigies of valor with a sabre given him by Louis XIV." Between 30 and 40 persons were killed or taken captive in this raid; 16 of the slain

---

[27] History Of New France, by Charlevoix (p 207): "Nescambiouit, who had returned from France the year before, always fought near the commandants; performing wonders with the sabre presented to him by the King. He received a musket-ball in the foot. In the two actions we had eighteen men wounded, three Indians and five Frenchmen killed, among the last two young officers of great promise, Hertel de Chambly, Rouville's brother, and Vercheres." Then he goes on to describe the reaction of some of the prisoners taken to Montreal and records their comments as follows: "The captives praised highly the kind treatment shown them by their captors during the retreat, which was effected without accident after the encounter just mentioned and various incidents related of some of the officers and volunteers, were more honorable to them than the signal proofs they had given of their bravery. I was one of the first to learn them, because I was at Montreal, at the very port, when the party landed there about the middle of September. Great praise was given especially to the Sieur Dupuys, son of the Lieutenant Particulier of Quebec, who carried his humanity so far as to carry the daughter of the King's Lieutenant at Haverhill, a good part of the way, the girl being unable to walk."

were inhabitants of Haverhill. The soldiers were mostly from towns up the river. Had the pursuit been more bold and well-sustained, it is likely the whole party could have been scattered and the prisoners recovered.

During the raid, Chief Escumbuit was back in his element, fighting beside the French commanders and basking in their admiration. The only change was that his famous war club was replaced by the silver sabre given him by the French King.

The adrenaline still coursed through his body as they herded the prisoners into the woods north of Haverhill. Suddenly, the unexpected happened. The militia was following them and their musket fire was very effective against the retreating raiders.

Escumbuit dropped his load of plunder and turned to fire upon the pursuers. In the sharp skirmish that followed, men on both sides fell. When finally the English fire faltered, he looked at some of them retreating towards the town. An exultant cry rose in his throat as he turned to pick up his load to resume his march north.

He took one step when he received a blow to his left foot that dropped him like a felled deer, his backpack pitching to the ground in front of him. He turned his head and was amazed to see a hole in the side of his left moccasin from which blood began to ooze. Two Canadians, close to him, seeing his plight, immediately came to his aide. They lifted him up and resumed the retreat, leaving their packs on the ground.

For the first time in his life, panic ruled Escumbuit's thoughts:

"Something is wrong! Chief Escumbuit does not fall in battle! It is the enemy who must fall! They must not see me carried by others from the field of battle. I must walk!"

Removing his arms from the shoulders of his companions, he attempted to walk on his own. The overwhelming pain, however, dropped him to his knees immediately, his face displaying shock at the knowledge that he needed help to continue the retreat. They continued on for some time in this manner. When they were sure that the pursuit stopped, they dropped to the ground to catch their breath. They removed his blood-soaked moccasin to reveal an ugly wound. The ball had entered just below the left ankle and traveled forward. Strangely, the spent ball could been seen as a lump under the skin in the forward part of the foot. They had given him a large pull on a bottle of brandy after which they made a slight cut over the ball and levered it out with the point of a knife. Now, after dousing the wound with brandy, they tied a bandage about it.

Fearing pursuit, wounded or not, the party continued north. They improvised a pair of crutches for the old Chief and he kept up as best as he could in spite of the pain. Some of the other wounded had to be carried on crude litters and the prisoners, mostly women and young children, had to be driven to keep up. By the time they reached the Hampstead area, Escumbuit knew what he had to do.

There was no longer any choice between returning to Big Island Pond or continuing on to Canada with the party. Two of the fit Indians in the party helped him make it to his own small village on the island where, after being fed, the two hurried off to catch up with the main party.

Metaxta cleaned the wound and applied poultices designed to draw the poisons from inside the wound. The medicine man performed his incantations and magic outside the wigwam and brewed potions to heal the wound, all with little effect. It was time to take stock of the situation. The Chief was in a state of denial. He had never doubted his seeming immunity to death or serious injury in his life-long battle with the English. His reaction now was that this was all a big mistake, that the incantations and potions of the medicine man would somehow magically make his foot well again.

After many weeks, the wound healed, but the foot remained a rigid, a useless appendage at the end of his leg. Only then did he finally begin to accept the reality that he would never again charge the enemy, sabre aloft, running, dodging and jumping as before.

Gone were the thoughts of joining Montigny in his campaigns. Never again would his name be on the lips of those in the court of King Louis XIV. For a long time he insisted it would have been better if the ball had penetrated his skull or heart. It certainly would have been better than this. Mostly he wondered why his Manatou, the eagle, had failed him. And finally, as he began to think of all the things that happened since he returned from France, he began to wonder if he had offended his Manatou. What had he done wrong?

The various histories covering the border wars seem to close the book on Chief Escumbuit at this point. The typical comment is that, after being wounded during the Haverhill, Massachusetts raid in August of 1708, "he seems to have dropped out of sight," that is, until--but that comes later.

THE CHIEF'S LAST REQUEST 1727

The 19 years, since that fateful day in Haverhill, tested the stoicism of Chief Escumbuit to the limit. He was a driven individual, right from his earliest days in his Pigwacket Village where he almost killed a play-mate because the boy stole and broke his flint knife in an effort to taunt him; only the intervention of some squaws prevented him from killing the boy by smashing his head on the same log in which the boy had snapped off the tip of his knife.

The fear and respect this outburst created in his friends left an indelible impression on the young Escumbuit, controlling his life from that point forward. He learned that being the most courageous, cruel, and aggressive of his peers brought him respect, if not love and friendship.

Like a rocket, his raw ambition and drive propelled him to great heights where, like the rocket, he blossomed in the Court of Louis XIV, King of France. Then, like the same rocket still glowing in its final spiral to earth, he flared once more in the Haverhill raid and, then, to be extinguished. Like an animal predator with a crushed foot, he could no longer do what he was created to do: to stalk and pounce with frightening speed in finishing off his kill. Now he had to depend on others to survive where, before, he needed no one. But nature has a way of compensating.

His second wife, Metaxta, was the medicine Escumbuit needed to make the adjustment to his new life. The marriage--which had come out of his need to be part of a family unit, and her need to replace her fallen mate--matured into a rewarding relationship.

Metaxta knew of his fame as a warrior. In the nurturing way of women, she ignored his fall from grace and his lame foot, even though she felt compassion for him. This relationship gradually grew stronger during the 19 years since the ill-fated raid at Haverhill.

Escumbuit gradually mellowed in the warmth of his small family: his wife, Metaxta, their daughter, Ramona, and his granddaughter, Bluebird.

Ramona's husband, Hinkum, was named for the Canadian gray goose; for, he was a steady provider. He was very proud to be related to a famous warrior like Chief Escumbuit.

Over the years, this isolated band of Indians dwindled from about 50 members to only four families with a total of 31 people. Their original Chief died and Escumbuit was named to replace him as Civil Chief. One of the first things he did was to hold a tribal meeting, proposing to move the tribe from their home on the big island to the smaller island, now known as Escumbuit Island. His military eye calculated the potential for surprise attack on the big island and decided it was too large an area for the tribe to defend.

He described how an enemy would have to approach the small island from the main-land and cross over the marshy channel to reach the island, pointing out that they were protected to their north, east and south by water, that they had only the narrow channel to defend. If they had to flee, they could take to their canoes and go either to the large island or paddle to the north end of the lake. Having seen the wisdom of his thoughts, some of them concluded by rationalizing that they would be closer to their garden at the outlet of the lake.

Although during those 19 years the border war continued, this small band was left undisturbed, thanks to the pattern of expansion by the settlers moving into the interior via the many rivers in the area. For instance, the outlet to the pond furnished a tributary to the Merrimac, but was too small to invite exploration by the settlers. This small band of Indians, therefore, found a pocket of territory not yet being contested by their white neighbors.

The signing of the Treaty of Utrecht, in which Louis XIV ceded much of the Indian territories in Maine and New Hampshire to the English, spurred the Indians to seek a treaty of their own. Their treaty, Submission and Pacification of the Eastern Indians, was signed July 13, 1713. Encouraged by that treaty, the settlers began to build trading posts, fisheries and even stone forts on the Saco, the Penobscot and the Kennebec Rivers. However, the borders were never completely at peace.

The war, known as Dummer's War With The Eastern Abenakis, began in 1722 and continued to 1725. When one considers that King Phillip's War began in 1675, and the Seven Year War ending in 1763, we are looking at a war that continued for about 80 years under different names, interspersed by lulls and battles.

It is very difficult to find any period during that time when one could say there was absolute peace.

Many attempts were made to exchange prisoners. The communications and transportation, being limited to sailing ships and good old fashioned walking, made this a very difficult problem to solve. One such attempt is worth describing here.

On October 5, 1710, the French surrendered Fort Royal in Nova Scotia to the English. In the formal take-over of the Fort, each side paraded its colors, drank toasts to the English Queen and to the French King, in general conducting themselves in a civil manner. Arrangements were made to send the French Governor and 258 of his men to France on three ships, allowing the Governor to carry with him a considerable stock of wine, brandy, sugar, spices and other things, together with the common allowance. Since both sides were in good spirits, it was decided at a council of war to have the English Major Livingston join with the French trader Castin together with three Indian guides to travel to Quebec and treat with Governor Vaudrieul for a prisoner exchange.

When Livingston arrived at Castin's trading post, there were over 200 Indians there with two English prisoners, one of whom escaping and taking with him his Indian captor's musket and canoe. The exasperated Indian took Livingston by the throat and was about to drive his tomahawk into his skull when Castin intervened to save the day.

This trading post situated on Penobscot Bay makes it difficult for anyone to imagine how an Englishman, a Frenchman and three Indians headed cross-country for Canada in the face of the approaching winter. Two days on their journey, the Indian guide drowned when their canoe overturned, swept away in the river with all his possessions. The others traveled by land the rest of the way through thick forests, fording countless rivers and beset by stormy weather and fog. The cedar and spruce forest was so dense they had extreme difficulty making their way through. When their provisions gave out, they subsisted on what they could scrape off the frozen earth or from the bark of trees.

Having arrived in Quebec on December 16, they were finally royally entertained by the French Governor. After discussing the prisoner exchange, he sent two Canadians with them for the return trip to Boston to continue the talks. Six days homeward bound, one of the Canadians took sick and was left at a place named Troy River. After arriving in Chamblee, they took three birch bark canoes which they carried for 70 miles over land through the woods and ice, finally using them for 60 miles crossing Lake Champlain, arriving in Albany, New York on February 23. Nothing was concluded with this attempt to exchange prisoners.

It is difficult to imagine people making a 70-mile portage with canoes. This well-traveled route to Canada was famous for what the Indians called *The long carry*. It must not be forgotten that the canoe was as important to the Indians then as the automobile is to us today. It was the Indians' main mode of transportation. An 18-foot birch bark canoe weighed about 80 pounds, and carrying it was like carrying a ten-year-old on one's back, but much more awkward.

Returning to Chief Escumbuit at Big Island Pond, it was the year 1727. He had stalled Captain John Newsholm's quest for the silver mine for a long time. Even after learning about the big battle between Captain Lovewell and the Pigwackets in 1725, he was not convinced the Pigwackets were gone. The captain was sure Escumbuit would go with him in the summer of 1726, but again he had refused, his response as always:

"The Pigwackets will not leave the land of their ancestors. When the white man goes to the Pigwacket village, my people go to the forest. They are still there, but the white man cannot find him. Only I can tell you if the Pigwacket have gone to Canada."

When the Chief was forced out of the Pigwacket tribe in 1707, his pension from the French King was cut off. The money was being forwarded to Father Bosquette from Quebec together with his own Jesuit salary, but the Jesuit did not know how to get the money to Escumbuit. Nevertheless, he faithfully saved the money for some time. When the Treaty of Utrecht was signed in 1712, the payments to Chief Escumbuit were discontinued by the crown. In effect--they wrote the Indians off.

The Indians never realized that the French King had ceded much of their land to the British crown in that treaty. When the Indians signed the Treaty of Submission in 1713, historians agree that the Indians never really understood how it affected their ownership of their land. Their outrage at being told they were living on land given to the British by the French King was the reason for the renewal of hostilities in 1722.

In April 1727, Ramona's husband, Hinkum, came to Escumbuit with a plan. Having discussed it with Metaxta and Ramona beforehand, they agreed that something should be done to ease the Chief's worry over his silver mine. Hinkum opened the subject, cautiously:

"Chief, your family is happy on this island. The English do not trouble us; we have enough to eat and we have peace in our small tribe. But we know the thoughts of your silver mine trouble you and we wish for your mind to be at rest. I will go to the land of the Pigwacket to see if they are truly gone. If I find they have left their homeland, I will go down the Saco to where Newsholm has built his trading post. There I can deliver any message you want me to give him. I want nothing for myself. I offer to do this for my wife and her mother. We want you to be happy."

The Chief turned it over in his mind for a few days and finally called Metaxta and her daughter to him:

"Ramona, you have married well. Hinkum is a fine brave. When I have warm thoughts in my breast for my family, he is as one with you and Bluebird. Tell him the time has come for me to act. I am no longer young. If I die, the secret of the silver mine will die with me. You both have made my life happy when I could have been sad. It is right that you should share the silver mine with me if Newsholm can arrange to sell the silver. It is for you and our family that I wish to take the risk."

Metaxta studied his face for a moment, then replied:

"No, my husband, it is you who have made *our* life complete. Without the silver it would be the same." The Chief looked at her, speechless, until she broke the silence: "Now, I must go and prepare our meal."

He sat on the knoll of Escumbuit Island facing west, on a beautiful clear spring day visited by a light breeze coming down the lake from the northwest--the birds busy with their mating and nesting activities as were the squirrels and chipmunks. As Escumbuit sat on pine needles smoking his pipe, he heard only the sounds of birds calling and the occasional chittering of the chipmunks darting about, while the light breeze startled the tiny birch leaves into a shimmering dance. High above, the outer boughs of the pines swayed gently; but, otherwise, everything was still. The late afternoon sun was bright and warm on his face from its low position above the hill on the mainland. The massive trunks of the pine trees between him and the lake were black silhouettes against the sun's brilliant reflection from the lake. The fronts of these same pines were bathed in the golden light of the sun. As the sun approached the crest of the distant hill, it dropped behind a wispy cloud on the horizon, changing the reflection on the lake from silver to gold. He watched this golden pathway evolving. For a moment, it seemed to shine bright. Then, suddenly, there was a flowing river of lavender rippling down its center. As the sun touched the dark edge of the hill, the lavender faded and the gold turned to copper, and then finally to pewter. The sun had set while the Chief sat motionless, riveted by what he had just experienced.

As an elder, entering the September of his life, his thoughts increasingly turned to his mortality. His belief in an after-life was as firm as that of the most dedicated religious devotée. As he sat, transfixed by the magical reflection of the sun on the lake, he felt in communion with the Great Indian Spirit, seeing the pageant of colors as an omen for the future--his future--and for that of his personal spirit.

"Though I have lived through more than 60 winters, there are still mysteries I cannot divine. The Great Spirit gives us evil as well as good spirits to guide us. We know that when an Indian drowns he is pulled to the depths of the lake by bad spirits. Some of our ancestors did not accept the counsel of our Great Spirit; their bones at the site of their villages are proof that they heeded these evil spirits,[28] and our Shaman warns us to avoid this place as well as the stone village to the south. All Indians know that Gluskap can fly from the north to the south pole in a single day and can change the size and the shape of animals as he pleases; yet, the forces of evil have powerful magic as well. Our Shaman tells us that the stone village to the south is the powwow place of evil spirits since only they have the magical strength needed to lift the huge stones which form this place? Our Shaman tells me that these evil spirits live deep in the earth and they come forth through the deep holes in the ground at their village. The great flat stone with its groove to carry the blood of their sacrifice warns the Indian to avoid this accursed

---

[28] Town Of Hampstead New Hampshire, 225th Anniversary edition 1749-1974: "By 1617 a "pestilence" or "plague" hit the New England coast, wiping out a great many of the Indians. Consequently, by 1620, there were large sections near the coast where only a few Indians remained. The early explorers of this section (the Hampstead-Atkinson area) reported finding bleached skeletons of Indians lying unburied around their camp sites. Other historians say that some villages lost up to 80% of their population and that the survivors were unable to handle the task of burying their dead. The survivors, influenced by their own superstitions about good and bad spirits, and who failed to grasp that their people had fallen prey to a white man carried illness, shunned the areas where the death toll had been greatest. Hampstead was one of the avoided areas, but according to records, never suffered from any Indian troubles."

place.[29] These evil places are created by the Great Spirit to exhort his people to follow his *good* teachings which tell them how they must inhabit the earth and how they must obey the signs of his good spirits."

He hardly noticed that his grand-daughter, Bluebird, had approached and taken a seat on the pine needles at his side. They sat in silence, the distant call of a loon coming down the lake. On hearing that haunting call, he seemed mesmerized.

"The bird is calling Gluskap."

"Why does he do that?" Bluebird asked. She heard the Indian myth before, but wanted to hear it again from her grandfather's mouth. He answered her by asking another question:

"Do you know why loons don't get stuck in the bottom weeds of the lake?" Without waiting for her answer, he began recounting the myth:

"One day, Gluskap decided to travel from Newfoundland across to Maine and into what is now called New Hampshire. Along the way, he saw a loon flying out over the water. It circled the lake twice, low near the shore where men and animals were, as if it were looking for something.

---

[29] Author's note: Escumbuit refers to a site located less than a mile south of the lake known as America's Stone Henge. Contrary to Escumbuit's fears, modern archeologists agree that this site was built to celebrate some sort of religious ritual. While these experts have declared this site to be a genuine archeological site, featuring an astronomical calendar, the original builders have not yet been positively identified. Carbon datings, however, have shown that the site is at least 5,000 years old. One theory supports the view that this site was constructed by Chief Escumbuit's own ancestors. Other scholars contend that the original builders came from Europe. It is a fascinating puzzle awaiting a solution.

"Gluskap called out: 'What are you doing?' The loon said, 'I was looking for you. I want to be your servant.' So, right away, Gluskap taught the bird a strange cry. The loon quickly tried it out. 'What is that echoing cry?' the loon asked.

"'That's you!' said Gluskap. 'How can it be coming from me, and still sound as if it's in the distance?' the loon asked. 'It's the way I made it, that's why', Gluskap answered.

"Now, Gluskap began to travel again and happened upon an Indian village, whose people were happy to see him. They gave him many gifts; they sang songs; and, they showed Gluskap a good time. They celebrated so much that Gluskap was so pleased that he turned them all into loons, who, to this day, continue to be faithful to Gluskap.

"That's why New Hampshire has loons. Even today, many people go at night by a loon's lake 'to hear the loon calling to Gluskap', or, 'a bird is looning to Gluskap', or, 'a loon is in need of Gluskap', or, 'Gluskap is riding in on a loon's call', or, 'there's no mistaking, Gluskap and the loon are talking to each other'.

"One day, the loon, who was the best of divers, got stuck at the bottom of the lake. The loon called out but could not be heard because its voice did not break to the surface of the water. The loon was stuck, and soon, it would drown.

"Gluskap, wandering nearby, said to himself: 'I haven't heard the loon in quite some time.' He listened hard, but did not hear any loon. He stood by the lake listening. But, no loon. It started to thunder. 'Shut up!' Gluskap exclaimed. 'I'm trying to hear the loon.'

"'Don't be angry,' the thunder answered. 'I'm trying to tell you that the loon is stuck in the weeds at the bottom of the lake.'

"Gluskap dove right into the water. There, at the bottom of the lake, he found the loon, nearly drowned. Gluskap grabbed the loon by its wings, and swam to the surface. As soon as they broke the surface of the water, the loon flew into the air, landing on the far side of the lake, and quickly began his usual calling.

"Gluskap answered: 'From now on, you can dive to the bottom of the lake, but not into the weeds.'

"So, my dear child," Chief Escombuit said, looking at Bluebird, "what you hear is the loon telling Gluskap that it didn't go into weeds at the bottom of the lake."[30]

The Chief and Bluebird were joined by her mother Ramona, who observed: "Hinkum is now on his trip two weeks. He should return soon. He has never been to the home of the Pigwacket. I am glad that our men do not go on the war path. I am happy when he is here on the island with us."

Escumbuit answered: "He will come back in not more than two days. If Gluskap wishes it, his news will be good news."

With that, the three walked to their wigwam at the point of the island where Metaxta was calling them for their evening meal.

---

[30] Derry News Article, Derry Library. In an article about Indian fables which had been translated by Howard Norman, Editor of Northern Tales is a fable entitled "Why Loons Don't Get Stuck Anymore In Bottom Weeds."

The next morning, after the women went off to the garden by the outlet of the lake, Escumbuit walked down to the end of the island where he knew two of the braves were building a canoe. As he approached, the two braves stopped their work for a moment to greet him and to inquire about his health. After acknowledging their greeting, he remarked on the canoe they were building.

"It is beautiful!" he remarked. "Where did you get that fine piece of birch bark you are now lacing over the frame?"

Menewa, animated, explained: "Such a piece of bark exists only in the far north where our hunters go to kill the moose. We found this tree during the moose hunt in January. We had to wait until March to fell it and take its bark for our canoe."

He then went on to describe how they got the piece of bark back to the island, saying that they waited until March, when the sap begins to run in the tree, before they could strip the bark from the tree. They took great care to drop the tree so that the bark would not be damaged, adding that after the tree was down, they propped up one end with stones so they could work on it at waist level.

First, they marked off the length of three Indians plus several spans of the hand for extra measure. They then made cuts around the trunk at these two extremes. On the top of the trunk, they joined these two cuts with a long straight cut. Then they carefully pried the bark away from the trunk using wooden wedges. By patiently inserting and tapping in a series of wedges, they were able to separate the bark from the tree in a single undamaged sheet.

Carefully opening up the curled piece of bark, they began to heat the inside of the bark using torches made out of scrap pieces of resin-loaded bark. By heating the moisture laden interior surface of the bark, it began to expand causing the bark to lie flat. After they got it flat, they reversed the natural curve of the bark so that the white exterior surface was on the inside of the roll.

The return trip took several days due to the long unwieldy piece of bark they were carrying--a piece of bark measuring about 19 feet long to be used to make a canoe about 18 feet long.

The two builders constructed a crude, shallow steaming bowl by laying a bed of clay and forming a depression long enough to immerse the longest pieces of wood to be formed into gunwales, bow, stern pieces and ribs of the canoe. They kept a fire going nearby on which they heated rocks and put the hot rocks in the water-filled steaming chamber to enable them to bend the various pieces of the canoe frame to the desired shape. These green pieces of wood were cut, steamed and finished in advance. Forms made from parts of old canoes were often used as patterns for the new ribs, gunwales, bow and stern pieces, using raw-hide thongs twisted with a stick to pull the wood into the proper shape.

They took an old canoe and place it on a flat space on the ground. Then they drove stakes into the ground to outline the form of the old canoe. After removing the old canoe, they placed the roll of bark, white side out, into this form where it was ready to be laced to the frame. As the bark was fitted to the frame, it was necessary to make v-cuts in the extreme edges of the bark to enable the canoe makers to gather the bark to fit the rounded frame as one would tuck and fold paper in gift wrapping a rounded object. After making wedge shaped cuts, the remaining bark was pulled together and overlapped and later waterproofed. This tailoring technique enabled the builders to fit the bark to a rounded frame. Although the bark was flexible in a general way, it could not be applied as one shapes Saran wrap to an irregular object.

Various green, straight grained woods were used to form the gunwales, keel, ribs, bow and stern pieces. Wide, thin basket splints were used as sheathing between the bark and the ribs to protect the interior of the bark from abrasion. Cedar was commonly used. It not only resisted rotting, but was very light. The spreaders or cross braces which divided the canoe into four sections and forming the support for the woven seats were made from tough hardwood such as maple. A finished 18-foot canoe weighed about 80 pounds. A canoe of this size and weight could be carried on the back of a single Indian.

Before the white man introduced the Indians to metal fastenings such as nails and screws, their canoes were assembled with natural lashings. The framing parts and bark were drilled and pierced with an awl and the canoe was held together with natural lashing made from the inner bark of the elm, basswood, or butternut trees.

If unable to find a birch tree sufficiently large to cover the canoe in a single piece, they would overlap smaller pieces to form the skin. The finished canoe was then made completely water-tight by applying a mixture of spruce resin mixed with tallow and colored with soot. This mixture stayed flexible when dry and would not crack like pure pitch.[31]

The finished canoe was often decorated by etching the owner's totem on its bow. By lightly cutting away the outer white bark and exposing the dark inner bark, they created intricate designs on the canoe. On some of the larger lakes where they were used to carry cargo, much larger canoes were built, some having a capacity of a couple of tons with the space to carry five or six Indians.

On these larger lakes the Indians also built cargo dug-outs made from the trunks of very large pine trees. Before obtaining metal tools, the Indians built small fires along the top surface of the trunk. They then gradually gouged out the charred wood with their stone axes and chisels to form the interior. When these dug-outs were not in use, the Indians sank them in shallow water using stones as weights. The water caused the wood to swell and stay water-tight. Several ancient Indian dug-outs were found submerged in swampy areas in Wolfboro and Meredith in the early part of this century.

A squaw came by to tell the Chief that Hinkum had returned from his trip. He immediately got up and began to walk with his limping gait towards his wigwam. Hinkum had already built up the fire over which a pot of stew was suspended and he now sat eating with great enjoyment having been on sparse provisions

---

[31] The Indian How Book, Arthur C. Parker, (pages 35-41) Details Indian canoe making.

for the past two weeks. After a quick greeting, the Chief motioned for him to finish eating before telling his news.

Finally, after loading his pipe, Hinkum sat and told the Chief what he learned during his trip up north and during his visit to Captain Newsholm on the Saco. The most important news was that there was not a single Pigwacket Indian in the old village. The palisade which had protected the central long house was still there, but the long-house was burned by the men who had followed Lovewell to the village. He met and talked with Indians from down the river, and they all told the same tale: "The Pigwackets have all gone to St. Francis and they are not coming back."

Captain Newsholm fed him well, giving Hinkum some tobacco and two bottles of rum to be carried to Chief Escumbuit as presents. The message sent with Hinkum was: "Tell the Chief that now is the time to claim the mine. The French King has given the English all the land in that area and we can buy the land that surrounds the mine with the right to take the trees for lumber and the minerals from the ground. Tell him I will be here to make a deal with him any time he wants to come."

Later that evening, as they sat around their campfire with a full moon shining down from the back of the island, Escumbuit spoke: "I have decided to go to the Saco River to meet with Newsholm, but I do not want to go alone. I want to travel slow because of my lame foot. Metaxta, I want you to come with me. Hinkum, Ramona and Bluebird must also come", he said, surprising them all by discarding his obsession for secrecy and deciding to include the entire family.

If they could have seen--this small group slowly making its way up the trail towards Saco the following week--any guess as to the purpose and the destination of their trip would have been far off the mark. They appeared to be a nomadic group of Indians in search of food, each carrying his large back pack hung from the shoulders and supported with the band of a tump-line around the forehead. Slowly but steadily, they walked northeast erecting temporary shelters for the night and occasionally accepting the hospitality of other Indians.

When they arrived at Newsholm's trading post, it was Escumbuit, who was worn out. The years of inactivity caused by his lame foot had taken its toll, wigwam smoke and pipe smoking surely contributing to his failing health. He was short of breath and tired easily. Furthemore, Chief Escumbuit was an old man suffering from emphysema.

John Newsholm greeted them warmly and fed them well. John was a single man used to simple surroundings and content to sleep in his own trading post. After the English turned down his application to build a trading post at Rollingsford because of his association with Escumbuit, he finally made a new application in his own name. This application was granted and the Chief bore him no ill-will at being left out of the deal. He existed where most white men would hesitate to live, his safety a delicate balance between the Indian's need to trade for English goods and their desire for English scalps.

The Chief decided that his entire family plus Newsholm would make the trip up the Saco River to the site of his old village. There, they would set up camp, and, he and Newsholm would make the final approach to the mine. After digging samples, they would return to the main camp, after which the entire party would make its way back down the river.

That night, Metaxta and her daughter questioned the Chief closely. "You are sure you want to take the trader to the mine? How can you be sure that Newsholm will do as he promises? Should you have the piece of paper which tells what your agreement is with Newsholm?" Finally, the Chief interrupted, saying: "I have now lived sixty two winters. I am an old man. How can I *ever* be sure that everything will be as I want it to be. I trust Newsholm more than any other white man, but hear me speak! *I do not have much time!* Now I listen to my Manatou who tells me that I must trust the pale face."

The next morning, they set out up the Saco in three canoes provided by Newsholm, who also supplied a store of food and two small tents which could be quickly erected to shelter them at night. The river's current was against them. But the canoes were light, they made steady progress up the river. Chief Escumbuit paddled like the rest. Although the paddling tired him badly, he did not complain. Finally, they beached the canoes at night. After he ate his second meal of the day, the Chief quickly fell asleep in his tent.

The canoes were well loaded with the tents, food and sleeping pads. Hinkum paddled one canoe with Bluebird in the bow. Metaxta and Ramona rotated positions in the second canoe while Chief Escumbuit exchanged seats occasionally with John Newsholm in the third canoe. On the third day, the river changed its course in a series of sweeping turns requiring them to paddle double the distance to their destination. They encountered some rain. But because they were all used to living out in the elements, it offered no special hardship to them.

Of the six travelers, the scenes along the river were familiar only to the Chief. With a 20-year lapse in time, however, even he saw changes in the otherwise familiar land marks. Finally, he signaled they had arrived at the site of his village, having recognized the bend of the river and the landscape.

The absence of canoes and of people gave him a curious empty feeling in his stomach. They beached the canoes and unloaded their gear. Before choosing a camping site, they walked up over the bank towards what once was the village of the Pigwacket Indians.

The Chief walked ahead of the rest until he reached a small elevation from which he could see the entire area covered by his former village. The empty feeling in his stomach was replaced by a wave of sadness which swept over him, filling his mind and his chest. Hinkum had described the village to him, but he was not prepared for the sight before him.

A skeleton of his former village marred the scene. Dotting the vast flat area were the rounded frames of abandoned wigwams, their bark coverings long removed or rotted away. Within the large palisade, once enclosing a series of longhouses, lay burned logs, charred ashes and a profusion of weeds. The palisade itself was broken in places like a fence with broken pickets. Surely, in a few years, the passage of time would also obliterate the evidence of a thriving people.

Where once lived more than 2,000 Pigwacket Indians, now, there was nothing--only trash and weeds.

After composing himself, the Chief finally walked the entire area with his family, pointing out where various activities had taken place. They sensed this was an emotional time for the old Chief. They simply let him conduct his tour and bare his thoughts. When they finished, they went back to where the Captain had set up the two tents.

Hinkum went off to the lake with his gun. When they heard a shot, they hoped he had bagged them some fresh game. After a second shot, he returned carrying two geese. The women prepared the food for their evening meal, and they ate sitting on the ground by the campfire with their plates on their laps. The men drank some rum and smoked their pipes, and again, Chief Escumbuit was first to retire to his tent. In the morning he and the Captain would head for the silver mine.

The next day, the Captain and the Chief loaded one of the tents and some food into a canoe and started up stream. The Chief told the others to expect them late on the third day. The family stood watching them off in their canoe.

As they headed up the river, the Chief realized he didn't want to leave them behind, even for three days. He still didn't feel well. But his Indian training, which required him to endure under the worse possible conditions, conditioned him to remain silent. Even though the pain in his upper arm and the tightness in his chest persisted, he did not mention it to anyone.

"Just three more days and we will be heading back down the river with the current at our back," he thought as he pulled on his paddle from the back seat of the canoe. There was little conversation between the two as they steadily paddled up stream.

They were a good team. The stern man normally guides the direction of the canoe with the person in the bow supplying power. Sometimes, however, if the current catches the bow of the canoe and swings it in the current, a good bow man will automatically switch sides to help the stern man to bring the canoe back on course. These two worked well together, instinctively making the adjustments to keep the canoe on a steady course without the need for verbal instructions.

Suddenly, Newsholm felt the canoe veer off course as the current caught the right side of the bow, pointing them out into the center of the river. He turned to see why Escumbuit had failed to bring them back on course. On seeing the distressed look on the Chief's face, Newsholm knew that something was wrong.

"Are you all right?" Newsholm asked.

The Chief gasped, "I have a pain."

"Stop paddling and stay where you are," Newsholm immediately ordered. "I'll bring us in to shore."

A big man, Newsholm slowly reversed himself in his seat. From his front position, he paddled the canoe stern first over to the shore; then, pulling the canoe with Escumbuit in it up on the bank, Newsholm lowered the Chief to the ground by supporting him from behind. He then went back to the canoe, secured a bottle of his standard medicine and told the Chief to swallow directly from his bottle of rum.

Recognizing that his companion was suffering from either angina pain or a potential heart attack, Captain Newsholm decided they would not go ahead to reach the mine. There just was no thought of continuing on to the mine now in spite of the Chief's protestation that he would be all right after a rest.

In the next half hour, the Captain made his decision and told the Chief what they were going to do. He arranged the tent on the bottom of the canoe and pulled it up beside the Chief. Now, he half lifted, half rolled the Chief into the canoe where he had him lie on his back with his head to the stern. Then the Captain slid the canoe back into the water, heading down stream to the village. When they arrived, three hours later, Newsholm pulled the canoe out of the water, cautioning the Chief to stay in his position until he brought the others. Fashioning a crude litter from two poles and some sail cloth, they carried him up to the tent.

By the time they brought the other tent from the canoe and set it up, the day was spent and they all sat down to decide what they were going to do next.

The Chief was made as comfortable as possible in the tent, showing no desire to get up from his pallet. He still had pain. After resting awhile, the pain subsided. He asked Metaxta to send Newsholm in. After the Captain got himself settled on the ground beside the pallet, Escumbuit spoke.

"Captain John, I cannot go to the silver mine with you. While I still live and while my mind is still clear, I wish to tell you how to find the mine. First I want you to swear in the name of your Great Spirit that you will honor the contract we made and share the silver with me, even if I am sick in my village, and that if I die, you will honor the contract with my wife Metaxta, my daughter Ramona and her daughter Bluebird."

John Newsholm, lifting his right hand, answered:

"I swear by Almighty God to honor the contract agreed to by myself and Chief Escumbuit. If he should die, I will honor the contract in the same way to the three women of his family. If I should fail to keep my word spoken to Chief Escumbuit, may Almighty God strike me dead where I stand, so help me God."

With this, the Chief began to give the directions to the mine as best as his memory would serve after an absence of 20 years. He described it in great detail, including the crucial sighting of a distant lone pine on a low hill and its intersection with the peak of Mount Washington in the distance. At that intersection, he was to direct his canoe on that line to the shore. From there the mine was only a quarter mile up the hill. The captain couldn't be sure he had all the information needed to find the mine. Since it was obvious the Chief was doing his best to give him the details, the Captain was satisfied with what he had--at least for now.

After a drink of rum to seal the agreement, the Chief asked his family to come into the tent. Metaxta wanted him to rest, but he raised his hand in protest.

"There are things I must say while there is time." He seemed stronger and more alert; yet, there was an urgency about him that only he understood. When they were all seated on the ground at his side he continued. "My Manatou told me to bring you on this trip with me. I told him there was no need for you to come, but he said, 'Bring them--you will need them.' Once, many years ago, I failed to heed my Manatou; that is why I had to leave this land. But my Manatou was deceived. Through the loss of my home with the Pigwackets, I found you. Maybe I did not hear him well. Maybe he wanted to guide me to you all the time", he said, pensively, then told them of the oath Captain Newsholm took and how the oath served them, and closing the subject by adding, "Captain Newsholm is our only hope. I have no other way to protect you. He will do what is right."

The Chief closed his eyes for a few moments, seeming to drop off in sleep. When his eyes opened again, he began to reveal his deepest thoughts in a rambling monologue:

"We must go home to our island tomorrow. I do not have the strength to do the things we came here for. If the Great Spirit calls me now I am ready, but my wish is to begin that journey from our island home. I want to be buried where the setting sun shows the golden trail to the other side. When my spirit walks that trail he must have my sabre to protect him against the evil ones who would lead him to darkness. I do not wish to be buried here. If I die now, place my body on a great fire made by the logs of the palisade. Though my flesh be consumed by the fire, my spirit will stay with my bones until they are buried with my sabre and my cloak. My spirit must have my sabre for protection during the long journey to the special place created by our Great Spirit."

He closed his eyes again as his family sat in silence watching his chest rise and fall rhythmically. Suddenly he spoke again in a different tone, as if from a distance.

"Hear me speak, my family. I am like an old oak battered by countless storms. Though the winds and frost have stripped me of my leaves and though my branches are weak, I still stand. But, soon, even the oak falls!

"In my youth, when I was called Ottucke--only I had the strength to string my bow; then my arrows killed game beyond the reach of others. The English trembled at the sound of my war-whoop, and the scalping cry of Escumbuit ringing from the Merrimac River to Newfoundland. The scalps on my cloak told the story of why I was named Assacumbuit--'He who is raised so high by his merit that thoughts cannot reach his greatness.'

"We burned their villages; we took a thousand scalps, we carried off their women and their children. Still, they came to steal our land. Our Shaman used their most potent magic against them, but their sorcery was stronger.

"I won many honors with the French. Their generals wanted only Escumbuit at their side in battle. The French King touched me with his sword and made me his knight. Yet, the French have forsaken our people and their treaty gives the land of my ancestors to the English. Now, we fight alone against the English, who multiply like leaves in the forest. I remember the things I saw in France!

"I, who as a boy killed the bear with my war-club; I, whom no warrior could defeat; I, who, having received counsel from the Great Spirit--I, I was unable to vanquish the paleface.

"How long can the old oak survive returning storms? See how it trembles!" he exclaimed faintly, turning his hand toward his body. "Soon, it will fall!

"The birds and squirrels will forsake it and the ant and the worm will consume it!

"So, think, my family, of what I say: the Great Spirit speaks through me now.

"Peace with the paleface is the only hope for our people. The paleface comes each year in greater numbers with their ships and their cannons. As our numbers dwindle, theirs multiply like the mushroom in the forest. Soon, they will till our gardens with their horses and plows. Our forests will fall for their dwellings. The deer, the moose and the bear will be driven from our hunting grounds and the stone buildings of the paleface shall occupy our fishing places.

"The flight of my people to Canada tells me these things will come to pass as surely as the sun rises each morning over the People of the Dawn. We see it in the village the paleface call Derryfield.

"Soon these people may want to fish and live at our lake. How can we refuse them? Our warriors are few and our will to fight falters. Now, the fierce north wind blows! It feels cold! The old oak is weak, its branches falling to the ground, its sap no longer rising.

"It is leaning and about to fall!

"The Great Spirit wills me to heed his voice: without peace our people are lost. It is my command that you must obey. It is my request--Escumbuit's last wish."[32]

With those words, Chief Escumbuit closed his eyes and spoke no more.

---

[32] History of the American Indians in the Manchester, New Hampshire Area, Thaddeous Piotrowski, Ph.D. (p. 16-48) Oak tree analogy taken from Passaconaway's farewell speech.

Top: Site of Pigwacket Village, Fryeburg, Maine. Bottom: Stonehenge--Sacrificial Stone, Salem, New Hampshire.

EPILOGUE

The story of Chief Escumbuit's journey from an isolated tribe in the wilds of Maine to the lavish French court of King Louis XIV at Versailles tests our credibility.

The Pigwacket Tribe into which Escumbuit was born began to emerge from its Stone Age culture a mere 20 years before he was born. About that time, the first traders made contact with them, introducing them to such marvels as metal pots for cooking, metal axes to cut down trees, and muskets whose noise and smoke dealt death to animals and men alike.

Until about 1640, the only threat to the Abenaki Indians came from other Indians, who settled their grievances with war clubs, cut from trees, and bows and arrows. That one of those Indians should have grown to maturity in that culture, and end up responsible for the death of 150 English settlers, then go to France to be knighted and given a silver sabre is remarkable.

Nevertheless, all of the principal facts in this story are confirmed in historical accounts of this period of history. Chief Escumbuit was born a Pigwacket Indian in the area we now call Fryeburg, Maine. He did fight with the French against the English settlers and he did run up a tally of over 150 victims. The quotations from the French historian Charlevoix, the Englishmen Penhallow, Parkman and Drake attest to Escumbuit's campaigns with Montigny and D'Iberville. He was received in the Court of King Louis XIV at Versailles in 1707. On his return to his people, he was driven from the Pigwacket tribe. Finally, a musket ball to his foot in Haverhill in 1708 ended his fighting career.

The climax of the story in which the chief dies, while taking an English trader to his silver mine far up the Saco River, seems to stretch the facts beyond belief. Of special interest in this regard is material taken from a 1939 book entitled *The Border Wars of New England* by Samuel Adams Drake.

At the end of his chapter on the sack of Haverhill, Massachusetts in 1708, there is a paragraph and a footnote worth reading.[33]

---

[33] "In this lively combat, two French officers, Chambly and Vercheres, were killed, and in the various encounters of the day the French admit that eighteen of their number were wounded. Their accounts add that the monster Assacumbuit performed prodigies of valor with a sabre given him by Louis XIV."

"As a mark of the royal favor for having, as he declared, slain one hundred and fifty of His Majesty's enemies with his own hand. How many were women and children he did not say. He was wounded in the foot in the raid, and very soon disappears from view. *The New England Weekly Journal* of June 19, 1727, has the following notice of his death;" "We hear from the eastward that some days ago died there Old Escumbuit, who was formerly the principal sagamore of the (now dispersed) tribe of Saco or Pigwacket Indians....He, Hercules-like, had a famous club, which he always carried with him, and on which he made ninety-eight notches, being the number of Englishmen that he had killed with his own hands.... He had formerly made discovery of a very fine silver mine up Saco River, but could never be persuaded to tell whereabouts it was till very lately he was prevailed with to promise to carry an Englishman (who had several times been in quest of it) to the spot, and endeavored to do it. But upon their way, when they got within a few miles of it, he fell sick, and in a short time died;

The product of six months of research and reading could have easily been condensed into eight or ten pages entitled, *Historical Facts On The Life Of Chief Escumbuit-Pigwacket Indian*. I chose instead to expand the facts into a story about how a young brave named Ottucke (The deer) came to be named Chief Escumbuit and how his prodigious feats as a warrior carried him to the Court of King Louis XIV. Reading about this warrior's life, one can be both repelled of the man, and at the same time be in awe of him. I was pulled in both directions by the story. In the end, as he died in his tent attended by his family, I felt only sadness.

Chief Escumbuit's instructions to his family that he be buried with his sabre facing the golden path of the setting sun on Escumbuit Island revealed his Indian belief that the Great Indian Spirit has retained a special place for his Indian race. He believed in his immortality and of the evil forces present on the final trail to that special place. He did not feel any guilt for his past deeds, but believed that his spirit would go, sabre-in-hand, just as he did throughout his turbulent life.

The Indians of northern New England were finally subdued in 1763 after almost a century of fighting the white settlers in their homeland.

King George's War, known as the War of the Austrian Succession, lasted from 1740 to 1748 and the French and Indian War, also called the Seven Year War, was fought from 1755 to 1763. The most surpris-

---

having first gave the Englishman all the directions he was able for the finding out of said mine, who is resolved to prosecute the matter, hoping still to make discovery of it."

ing fact is that the Abenaki Indians, who numbered not more than 10 to 12 thousand when the settlers arrived, were able to resist the advances of the civilized white man for almost 100 years.

In the years following the death of Escumbuit, the settlers gradually pushed northward into New Hampshire. The shores of the lake we now call Big Island Pond were eventually touched by the townships of Atkinson, Derry, and Hampstead. In the late 1700's someone described it as "that lake where Chief Escumbuit lived". Later, it was referred to as *Escumbuit's Lake*; finally, *Lake Escumbuit*. Copies of two 1926 picture post cards, furnished by Patsy Goodridge, describe it as Lake Escumbuit. From that point, the name Big Island Pond seems to have taken hold and the little four acre island opposite Chase's Grove became known as Escumbuit Island.

From the knoll on the west shore of that island, in the late afternoon of certain summer days, the lake still reflects a shimmering path of gold and lavender on which Chief Escumbuit imagined his spirit striding westward to the special place created by the Great Indian Spirit. If one were to listen carefully, he or she might hear the distant lonely cry of the loon calling out to Gluskap, giving thanks for having saved him from the swaying entangling bottom weeds of the lake.

REFERENCES

History Of The Indian Wars, Samuel Penhallow Esq. 1726

History and General Description Of New France, Rev. P.F.X. de Charlevois, S.J.

Journal Of Voyage To North America, Rev. P.F.X. de Charlevois, S.J.

France and England In North America, Francis Parkman, 1910

The Border Wars Of New England, Samuel Adams Drake

Pigwacket, George Hill Evans

Histoire Des Abenakis, N.F. Marault

Historical Sketches of Andover, Sarah Loring Bailey, 1880

Andover: Symbol of New England, Claude M. Fuess, 1959

Colby's Indian History, Solon B. Colby

Indian Place Names Of New Hampshire, John C. Hudon, 1962

The Indian How Book, Arthur C. Parker

The Abenaki, Colin G. Callaway, 1953

Who Was Who In Native New England History, Carl Waldman, 1990

How The Indians Really Lived, Gordon C. Baldwin

History Of The American Indians In The Manchester Area, Thaddeus Peotrowski, Ph.D.

Town Of Hampstead, New Hampshire, 225 Anniversary 1749-1974, Hampstead Library
Handbook Of North American Indians, Vol 15, Smithsonian Institute, W.C. Sturtevant, editor
Abenaki, Gordon Day
The Expeditions of John Lovewell, Frederick Kidder, 1804-1885
Encyclopedia Of North American Indian Tribes, Bill Yenne
Historic Indian Trails Of New England, Chester B. Price, 1974
Derry News Article (Derry Library)--Translation Of Indian Legends, Howard Norman
Indian Wars Of New England, Herbert Milton Sylvester
From Turnpike To Interstate, Derry Historical Society, 1827-1977
Song of Courage, Song of Freedom, Marilyn Seguin, Branden Publishing Co., Boston, 1993
The Forts of Maine, 1607-1945, Robert L. Bradley, Ph.D.

Index